BANTAMS

BANTAMS

David Kay

David & Charles
Newton Abbot London North Pomfret (Vt)

British Library Cataloguing in Publication Data

Kay, David
Bantams.
1. Bantams
I. Title
636.5′871 SF489.B2

ISBN 0–7153–8395–7

Photoset in Times by
Northern Phototypesetting Co Bolton
and printed in Great Britain by
A. Wheaton & Co Exeter
for David & Charles (Publishers) Limited
Brunel House Newton Abbot Devon

**Published in the United States of America
by David & Charles Inc
North Pomfret Vermont 05053 USA**

Contents

Introduction

Not many years ago, most farms and smallholdings would have a few hens and a cockerel scratching around a couple of hen cabins, but now, because of the advances in commercial poultry-keeping, this is a much rarer sight. One result has been that many of the well-known, traditional breeds of standard poultry have disappeared.

However, this has not been the case with bantams. These attractive and alert little birds have become very popular in recent years, and great progress has been made in the quality and quantity of birds being bred and exhibited. Today, they are an unforgettable part of our poultry shows, and people are starting to keep them as a fascinating and rewarding hobby.

This book deals with all the aspects of keeping bantams – from choosing a breed, right up to exhibiting at a championship show. It follows each stage in detail, describing the systems and practices which I have used successfully over many years, and I hope it will guide anyone taking up this hobby to the pinnacle of success – breeding a show champion!

1
Why Keep Bantams?

Bantams in one form or another have been bred for about 200 years. It is true to say that for a considerable part of this time standard-bred poultry were much more common, with bantams a specialist interest for a few people only. However, due to the expense involved in keeping large poultry, coupled with restrictions on space in small gardens, more and more people have switched to bantams and found them to be equally rewarding and interesting.

By opting to keep bantams, more birds can be kept on a given area and this in turn means that there is an opportunity to breed better stock, creating a most interesting and satisfying hobby – and eventually you might become a bantam exhibitor.

Obviously, the more space that is available, the more birds can be kept. Most houses have land at the side, or a large back garden which often takes the form of flowerbed, lawn and vegetable garden, with a certain amount of waste space at the bottom – often referred to as 'that patch of ground'. It is this patch that can be transformed from being a nuisance to its owner to something which can give a great deal of pleasure and satisfaction. Here there is normally sufficient space to keep bantams.

Comparing with standard poultry

It is worth looking at the basic differences between keeping standard-bred poultry and keeping bantams. One of the definite advantages of bantams is that they are so much cheaper to keep. Their food consumption is less, so their eggs, albeit somewhat smaller, are cheaper to produce. Again referring to that patch of ground, bantams do not make as much mess in the runs. In summer the ground does not become as bare and in winter it does not get so churned up in wet weather.

Bantams, too, are extremely attractive, full of charm and character. There are many different and mixed colours to choose from, with some breeds having the added attraction of a crest or feathered feet. Many breeds have distinctive markings. They can give an image of quality and pride on that specially converted patch of ground. How often does one see a poultry run where a misguided choice has been made – a number of crossbred hens lingering on a dreadful patch devoid of grass and strewn with rotting cabbage leaves? Bantams, properly kept, should never reach such a stage.

Bantams and children

There is something special about bantams in the eyes of young children. Standard-bred poultry tend to be referred to and seen as just 'hens', which lay the eggs that can be bought in the shop; but bantams are specially for them.

Keeping a few bantams at the bottom of the garden can be of great benefit to young children. They learn to care for them, as they do for other animals, and are taught aspects of nature and breeding. Caring for the birds means a set routine of feeding and the fun of collecting eggs at the end of the day; breeding provides all the excitement of chickens hatching and the fun of seeing them grow. Certain breeds, if carefully chosen – they are mentioned later in this book – can easily become pets. They can be picked up from the floor and handled and will readily become so tame that they will eat from children's hands quite safely. And not only are the birds an absorbing hobby for children, father or mother – a fairly regular supply of eggs is guaranteed, and with the birds having a certain amount of ground on which to roam the yolks are attractively deep in colour, something rarely seen these days.

A relaxing hobby

There are of course other reasons why bantams have been so much more popular recently. Many businessmen these days are advised by the medical profession to involve themselves in a hobby, and bantam-keeping has the advantage over gardening, yachting and photography in involving you for 365 days per year. This is, of course, something which often appeals to retired people; their bantams ensure that they get out of the house and into the fresh air at least every morning and evening, and provide an on-going interest.

One of the author's silver-spangled Hamburgh females, a London Championship winner

But involvement in bantams does not start and finish on the patch of ground at the bottom of the garden or the side of the house. Attendance at local poultry society meetings is advisable, and this of course could lead to exhibiting at the local show to compete for the much-sought-after prize cards and cups. When this happens, the picture is nearing completion. The whole household becomes totally and utterly involved. But before that far-distant stage is reached there are other bridges to cross. So let us go back to the beginning and start off!

2
Starting Off

Something that anyone beginning to think of keeping bantams should see is a bantam show. Here a big display of various breeds will hold your attention whether you already know something about them or not. You find yourself giving much thought to the question of which breed or breeds most appeal. You can ask many and varied questions at the show, and you will have the chance to get in touch with a local breeder and thus develop your enthusiasm further.

Selecting and buying stock

The selection of stock is of great importance, as is choosing the right breed. Consideration must be given to whether the surrounds of your property are suitable for housing a breed which may tend to be flighty. Alternatively, you may wish to keep a heavy breed, well known for producing rich brown eggs. Or you might prefer some of the attractive ornamental breeds, with their distinctive markings. In other words, you should get clearly and firmly in mind what you intend your bantams to be for – whether they are to be pets, whether you are more interested in good egg-layers, or whether you intend to go in for breeding show birds.

How many bantams should be bought, where and when? Having visited several and varied shows and decided on a breed, you must now choose which current exhibitor is the one most likely to be helpful. One particular exhibitor has probably been more forthcoming than others. He or she will be only too pleased to pass on assorted information and recommendations about a particular breed. If so, you would be wise to visit and talk to him or her further, with a view to buying some of the stock.

But do not try to buy the best stock – it is highly likely it would not be for sale anyway! Starting to keep bantams is not only exciting, it can also involve problems. The soundest possible advice is to buy good birds which are true representatives of their breed, but not so valuable that should an accident occur the loss

Old English Game spangled bantam hen – one of the most popular varieties

would be a major catastrophe. Walk before you run. If you are going to make mistakes it is better to make them with birds that have not cost a large sum. A new fancier should be fully experienced in keeping poultry through the four seasons before embarking on buying birds of greater value.

It is usual to start off with what is termed a 'trio', composed of a male and two females. Again there are arguments for and against the buying of older birds or birds of the current year's hatching. If you intend, or dream about, breeding bantams for showing, then aged birds are possibly the answer, because you can ask to see offspring which your trio have bred. This will give you some idea of the type of stock which you can expect to breed the following year – providing all goes well.

Alternatively, birds of the current year's hatching have everything before them – they are in all probability at least two years younger and consequently should have a longer breeding life. However it is advisable to breed only from birds aged two years and upwards: it is generally found that younger cockerels and pullets have insufficient stamina for the breeding pen.

Should you have decided to keep several different breeds of bantams mainly for their decorative appeal, you will need to bear in mind that some breeds tend to fight with each other. You should therefore seek professional advice as to which breeds will live happily together.

But what about buying growing stock? This is not to be recommended if you are going in for breeding and showing, because any breeder or dealer selling such stock would obviously not be including any potential show and breeding birds. His spare birds in this category will usually be those he considers will not make the grade. They may be too large, they may be too small, they may be too dark, they may be too light; in fact, not to be recommended unless you are wanting egg-layers or pets.

Buy birds, not eggs

Perhaps from a purely economic point of view, you may have thought of starting off by buying eggs for hatching. But again this is a method of starting which is well down the list. Every reputable breeder will use his or her best endeavours to sell hatching eggs that are truly fertile, but no guarantee can be given. Furthermore, the eggs can be shaken up during transportation, or problems can occur during the three-week incubation period, either with the incubator or the broody hen; then only half the eggs might hatch.

There could be further disappointment too, as all the chicks might turn out to be cockerels! Hatching eggs are not the answer.

The best recommendation therefore is to buy a trio. If at all possible, see what you are buying and be satisfied as to their age. It is of prime importance that the birds are in good condition, healthy with no deformities, and free of scale and mite – birds that you will be proud to care for and to display. It goes without saying that the birds of any particular breed must be truly representative of that breed, and you must be satisfied that they are in accordance with the breed standards, if you can determine that.

It is a good idea, as said earlier, to get to know the vendor, so that you can ask his or her advice on selecting your breeding stock, as well as opinions about your future breeding policy and help with any problems that may arise with that particular breed. You should find out what the birds have been fed on, as it is good practice to continue with the same food until the birds have settled in their new surroundings.

Finally, in this very important matter of buying stock, the onus must be on the purchaser to make it absolutely clear to the vendor what exactly the birds are for – whether they are for showing, or whether they are to be just pets running around in the garden. There is a very big difference between the price of a breeding trio that could well produce show champions and the price of healthy but mismarked specimens whose purpose in life is to provide a few eggs, look decorative and provide a pleasant hobby. If you find it difficult to secure exactly the right birds, then seek advice from the Secretary of the Poultry Club of Great Britain, whose name and address can be found through libraries and information bureaux. The Secretary will be happy to forward names of breeders in your area who specialise in the type of bird you require.

Transporting your birds

When going along to buy your birds, you will need a suitable container for carrying them. Far too often an old wooden crate or a box with holes in the bottom is produced: surely, if a considerable sum of money is being invested in the birds, they deserve something decent in which to travel. The ideal container is a specially made wickerwork poultry hamper lined with straw or hay, but a good strong cardboard box with a sufficient number of holes in the sides for ventilation will serve the purpose quite adequately. Birds can travel long distances when in a suitable container.

Their new home

Accommodation for your bantams is discussed in the next chapter. What happens when the birds arrive in their new home? It goes without saying that their accommodation should not only be clean and comfortable but free from all the various mites that can so easily affect stock. It is therefore a good practice to spray or dust all new arrivals with a recommended powder or aerosol spray around the vent area and under the wings. This will prevent them transferring any existing mites to their new premises.

At this stage you will be delighted and full of enthusiasm for your new hobby. It goes without saying that the family will be giving the birds a lot of attention and there will be a great temptation to invite your neighbours and friends to see them. You should resist this urge for the time being, in order to allow the birds a few days to settle in. They should be left alone in their surroundings and fed on the type of food they have been used to, along with a good supply of fresh clean water.

Soon the birds will appear to have settled and be ready to venture outside their home. It is good practice on the first few occasions to let them out a couple of hours before dusk, before the evening feed of mixed grain, so that at feeding time they will be somewhat hungry and eager to return to their house. This routine is necessary because if you give the birds complete freedom on their first day, it is likely that when darkness falls they will not have returned, simply because they have not yet found their way around. A search party will have to set out, and more often than not they will be found perched high on the branches of nearby trees or in similar awkward situations.

As time goes on, the birds can be let out that little bit earlier each day, and they will very quickly get to know and adapt to their surroundings. Now is the time to show them off to your neighbours and friends. You should of course be careful to keep dogs and cats out of sight at this stage, the main priority being to settle the birds and not let anything frighten them.

3
Management

Whilst you will find keeping bantams a fascinating hobby, nevertheless serious thought must be given to the financial aspects – in particular with regard to the birds' home and its immediate surroundings. It is important to glean as much information as possible about the types of cabin available and the various systems of management to use; you will learn a great deal about these things by visiting shows and other breeders' premises. Various hints and tips will be picked up, very often in sharp contrast to what you had in mind. You might hear breeders saying that a cabin would not have been so big, or a run so small, if the alternatives had been viewed before a decision was made.

Regrettably, the image of a poultry pen in many people's eyes is not highly appealing. Their minds turn to the type of poultry pen that is often seen from railway-carriage windows, on allotments on the outskirts of our towns and cities. These pens are too often not a good advertisement for the Fancy, though they may be the only housing that the owner can afford. However, if you are going to keep bantams then it is up to you to provide them with the best possible accommodation – if something is worth doing it is worth doing well.

Housing made out of tea chests; runs bounded by often rusty corrugated-iron sheets, pallets of various shapes and sizes, or ancient iron frames; old tins used as drinking vessels – all are unsuitable and will eventually attract vermin. These are the sorts of units that rats in particular find a comfortable home. 'Making do' is something that should not be encouraged nor practised.

Choosing the bantam house

When you have decided on the site for keeping your bantams, it is advisable that the piece of ground is accurately measured and that a plan is drawn to find the best possible layout. It is particularly important to consider the position of the pathway in relation to the proposed cabin so that it is not necessary to cross the pen each

How not to do it! Tin cans, pots and pans, old boots, car doors and rusty netting make this a paradise for vermin

time the birds are visited – in wet weather the ground surface would soon become a sloppy, muddy mess. Have the cabin door near a hard pathway. If due thought is given to this point, you will probably be able to attend to the birds while wearing your bedroom slippers rather than wellingtons!

Having assessed the piece of ground and the best position for the cabin, you must consider exactly which of the several types of house you can purchase will best serve your purpose. Obviously, finance must be taken into consideration as well as convenience: maybe you have the skill and knowledge to build your own. If you are buying, go to a reputable manufacturer, and if at all possible, have a look at the unit before you decide.

Whichever type of building is chosen, whether it is the standard type of poultry house or one of the smaller versions, it must be sufficiently robust to stand up to all kinds of weather and be built to last. Besides the standard type of cabin, there are also movable runs (see page 20) which have small living quarters at one end with a suitably enclosed run at the other in which the birds can move outside. However, we will assume that the standard type of cabin is your choice. These can be purchased in various sizes, the commonest being 8×6ft or 12×8ft; these will fulfil all your needs.

Whether it is a small or large size there are several important things that must be checked. As well as being robust, the cabin must be well ventilated. There must be windows that open, or an air vent in the roof. Flooring is also a vital element and should be made of wood. Some breeders use a concrete base but this practice is not recommended, because wood is much warmer (especially in winter). It is also recommended that the cabin should have a coat of creosote before it is delivered, thus ensuring that it arrives weatherproofed and free from insect life.

The roofing is very important. It should be felted, and is better without roof lights. These do give more light inside, of course, but if the building is of a standard design this should not be necessary.

Smaller cabins

It is of course perfectly possible to buy a smaller cabin. This can meet the general requirement although obviously will not give the same scope as the larger (12ft×8ft) size already described. Perches, dropping board and nest boxes will be there, but this does not compensate for the loss of space. Usually the smaller type of cabin has a sloping roof with a couple of windows or ventilation hatches at the front by the door. If this type of unit is purchased then the solid back must be placed against the direction of the sun to minimise the heat from its rays.

Movable runs

These can meet certain requirements but they are not the best type of unit for all-the-year-round work. They are ideal during the summer months for rearing young stock, and particularly for broody hens and chicks. But in the depth of winter they can be cold. Ventilation is not as good as in a standard unit and space is limited. Through experience, it has been generally found that the standard type of house is better.

Secondhand cabins

From regular advertisements in the local press, fanciers realise only too well that secondhand cabins can be bought at very competitive prices. However, whilst the cabins might be cheap the problems that they can create might be expensive. There are

Splendid example of a bantam unit at the bottom of a suburban garden

Three ideal runs

many disadvantages in buying secondhand cabins, not least the faulty structure too often found when they are dismantled. Areas of rotten boarding may not show when the cabin is still in place with its first owner, and secondly, the structure has to be transported to your site. Also, a cabin rarely goes up as well as it comes down . . . Not only can windows be broken but the roof can be damaged and this necessitates a complete re-felting operation, because it must be totally waterproof.

Another big disadvantage is that you are unlikely to know what has been kept in the cabin beforehand. There could have been birds in it with all sorts of diseases and here real trouble could be bought. In any case, for safety the whole structure must be disinfected and creosoted before re-erection.

Conversely, there have been many good cabins bought secondhand by satisfied purchasers. Providing the vendor is known and you are sure that his stock was disease-free, then you might find a bargain.

Dividing the cabin

It should be borne in mind that providing the cabin is large enough it will be possible to divide it into two equal-sized units by inserting a partition. This should have a built-in doorway to give access from one unit to the other. This modification is particularly useful when space is at a premium and it has several advantages. For instance, one unit can be cleaned and sterilised and left to dry completely whilst the birds live in the other section – providing there is adequate fresh air. Alternatively, one unit can be in use, with the bantams running out into an adjacent pen, whilst the second unit and its adjacent pen are being rested – particularly important in wet weather. You may like to keep your young stock in one unit and your breeding stock in the other. Furthermore, it is possible to run four separate outside pens from such a divided cabin, provided there are two 'pop holes' on each side of the cabin (one serving each run).

Erecting the cabin

Having decided exactly which type of cabin will suit your purpose there comes the problem of setting it up. Here again there are several important factors to take into consideration. As already

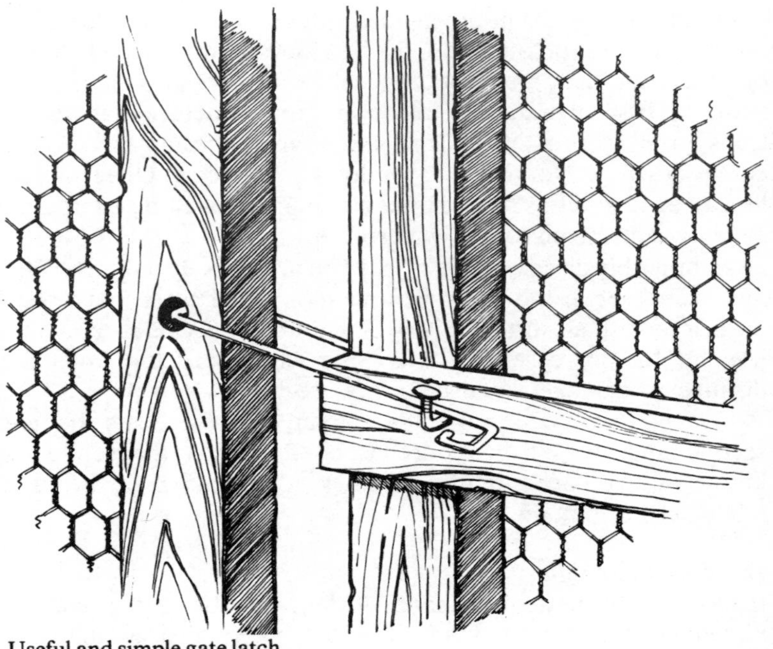

Useful and simple gate latch

mentioned, it is vital that the unit is sited in the most suitable position – in particular with good access pathways. The wooden floor must be placed sufficiently high off the ground to allow a terrier dog or a cat to get underneath, in case at some future date there are unwanted visitors! It is fatal to place the wooden flooring directly on to the ground because, as well as encouraging the wood to rot, this provides a breeding place for vermin – rats especially. If at all possible, the windows of the cabin should be out of direct sunlight; this is a great benefit in the summer, because warmth breeds the insects and mites that everyone wants to avoid, particularly in the birds' home.

Fittings

Besides the four walls, roof and floor there are other important fittings to a poultry house. Firstly, there is the perch. This is often referred to as the 'hens' bed' and is something that must have

Excellent bantam cabin set firmly off the ground and with adequate space

regular attention. A perch measuring 2×1in is ideal; and it should be movable. This is important, because if the perch cannot be removed, it becomes a perfect breeding ground for red mite; if it is not the right size then crooked breastbones can develop in the bantams and a bird with this deformity is automatically disqualified when exhibited. Below the perch it is advisable to have a dropping board of suitable size – to keep the bantams' droppings from the floor of the house; it must be cleaned regularly. The dropping board should be given a light covering of sawdust to make cleaning easier, and be refurbished with new sawdust after each cleaning.

Whichever sort of cabin is purchased, one necessary item is the 'stepladder', the small ladder from the ground to the 'pop hole' which the birds use to leave and re-enter their home.

It goes without saying that nest boxes are an important part of the bantam house. Two nest boxes per five bantams are usually sufficient, but there must be a minimum of two anyway. If two hens wish to lay at the same time, there will then be no squabble over nest boxes and no risk of broken eggs and the subsequent bad habit of egg eating. Each nest box should be about 1ft square, its base approximately 2ft off the ground. Again, this is to prevent inquisitive birds pecking at the eggs and developing the egg-eating habit. An old orange-box placed in the corner of the cabin on a couple of bricks is not a suitable nest box, as it will encourage these traits. The nest box must be comfortable and should be lined with hay or straw to make it attractive.

The permanent run

A permanent run must of course be erected round the ground where your bantams are to roam. The run can be divided into two parts to correspond with the pop holes from the cabin, but the most important points to consider are security and the placing of the gateway into the run in relation to the cabin. As said earlier, try to arrange to be able to get to the cabin without walking through the run, because otherwise a muddy track will develop there in winter, or any wet weather. It is advisable to have the door of the cabin adjacent to the garden's permanent hard pathway, so that the gateway to the run is only used in summer or in emergency.

The mesh of the netting round the run must of course be too small for the birds to push through. In days gone by a small trench some 4 or 5 inches deep was dug all round the pen boundary and the netting sunk in it; this did stop vermin digging under the netting and entering the pen. But with the high cost of netting today this can only be termed a luxury, and probably a better system is to forget the trench and to erect boarding or tin sheets all the way round the pen to a height of some 18 inches. This has a double benefit, keeping the wind off the bantams – especially important in breeds where great care of the lobes is needed – and, as you can nail the netting towards the top of the boards then less height of it is needed, giving some saving in cost.

The height of the fence surrounding the cabin really depends on the bantams being kept. All bantams will fly, especially when startled by a stray dog or cat, and it is impossible to say that any particular height will always be secure for all birds. Generally a fence of 5 to 6 feet will be adequate, but if total security is wanted then put netting over the top of the pen.

Equipment

Several other items of equipment are necessary. For food containers, you can buy galvanised troughs. Wooden ones can be made at home and are cheaper, but they are more liable to harbour disease, need scrubbing and disinfecting regularly and do not last as long as the metal ones.

Galvanised water fountains can also be bought from the same suppliers as the food troughs; look in the catalogue of any poultry appliance manufacturer. It is recommended that the standard type is chosen, though plastic fountains are available. Whichever you buy, make sure that all parts are easily accessible for cleaning; fountains should be cleaned at least once a month.

Another thing you need is a grit box. Again this is usually galvanised, and is placed in the corner of the cabin because it is less used. Many people believe that the birds need grit to help form the eggshell. Whilst this is true to some degree, the main purpose of giving birds grit is to aid digestion.

Galvanized water fountain (1gal)

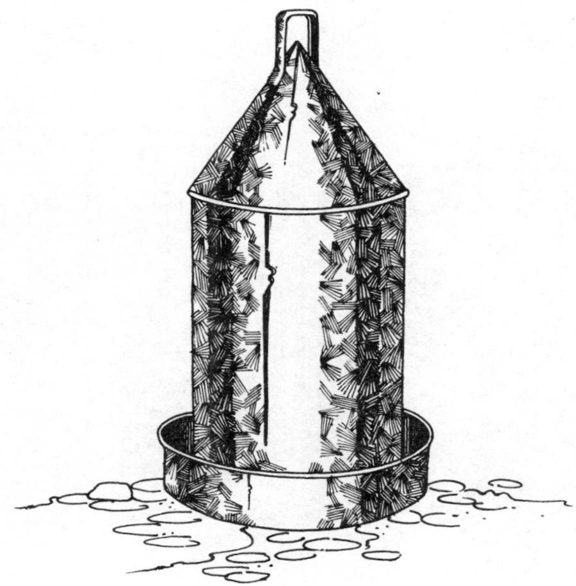

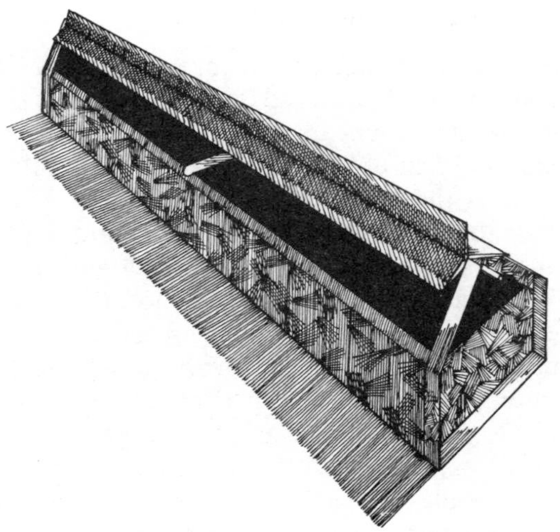

Feeding trough showing the swivel which prevents birds entering the trough and scratching out the food. It is galvanized for easier cleaning

Typical cabin interior with correctly positioned nest box, galvanized feeding trough, water fountain, dropping board and perch

Finally, you need litter, to cover the floor of the cabin to a depth of about 4in. The litter is normally sawdust but if possible mix it with some peat moss, and also with a few handfuls of lime which will help deter lice and red mite. It may be found that parts of the litter are not regularly turned over by the birds, which will have their favourite scratching places. So to prevent any unfavoured parts becoming stale, turn them over with a fork so that the litter is evenly spread around. It is good practice to fork all the litter into the centre of the cabin once every four or five weeks and let the birds scratch it out again. This method ensures good circulation of the litter, keeps it dry and prevents it from becoming stale. There is nothing worse than wet litter – and this is why it is so important to have a completely waterproof cabin. If you find wet litter, you should remove it immediately.

Feeding

There are no hard and fast rules as to what bantams should be given to eat, or the quantity, but there are guidelines as to the best form of food for optimum health and when it should be fed.

Feeding frequency

It is normal to feed bantams twice per day – early in the morning and just before dusk. But for various reasons there are times when feeding is restricted to just once per day: for instance if the bantam keeper is working on a shift which precludes twice-per-day feeding, during the short days of winter when it may not always be possible to be at home before dark to attend the birds. Whatever the situation, the birds should certainly be fed in the morning. When they come down off their perches they are hungry and looking for food, and if it is not readily available then all sorts of problems can start. They might start pecking each other and develop the feather-pecking habit, which in turn will draw blood and cause damage to the victim. Hunger will also encourage egg eating.

Food amounts

One of the questions a beginner always asks is how much food should the birds have? This is a question that cannot be given a precise answer, because it has to be judged from experience.

However, as a guide, remember that a bird's crop is something like the size of a small table-tennis ball and it requires filling at least once per day. It should not be crammed, otherwise the bird will become cropbound and problems will develop. This is the best yardstick that can be given. The approximate weight of the full crop is about one ounce. Another guideline is to give two clenched fistfuls of food to every three bantams, but again much can depend on the particular breed because some breeds do need more than others – and on the size of the fist!

Mash

The best arrangement is to feed the birds twice a day – a wet mash in the morning and mixed grain in the evening. The wet mash is normally a layers' mash or a breeders' mash, depending on the time of year. Whichever is currently in use should be purchased from a reputable corn merchant. The term 'wet mash' does not mean that the mash has to have so much water added that a sloppy mix results. A more realistic description would be 'damp mash' – it requires mixing with just sufficient water to dampen it so that it clings together. Into this mash any suitable scraps should be mixed – but most certainly not all the scraps that come from the kitchen waste. Giving mash in the morning is one of the best feeding systems for bantams. It ensures that they get the most nutritious food when they are at their hungriest, and have plenty of time to eat it. Mash of course does take longer to eat than grain – the birds have to peck at it continually to get their crops anything like full. It is a sure way of keeping them out of mischief. After the feeding of the mash, the bucket in which it was mixed should be quickly swilled out and put away tidily for the next occasion.

Scraps

Generally speaking, the only scraps to be given to the bantams are those which a human being would not object to eating. Things such as orange and lemon peel, banana skin, rhubarb leaves and horrible mouldy bread should be avoided like the plague. It is also advisable not to feed them carcases of chicken or the remains of the Sunday joint.

Whatever scraps are given, some always remain uneaten; these leftovers can cause problems, because they become smelly and are very attractive to vermin. The ideal scraps for mixing with the mash are such things as leftover potatoes, peas, bread crusts, stale biscuits and cake, etc.

Vegetables
Should you have such things as spare cabbages or turnips in the vegetable garden, these will do for the poultry. A good tip is not to throw them in the run, where they will be exposed to all sorts of weather and the birds will trample on them, but to hang them from the roof of the cabin. All that is required is a long string tied to the apex of the building with the cabbage or turnip hanging about six inches above the litter. The birds will fight shy of it to begin with, but after a few pecks will become used to it, and it is surprising how they will continually peck away at it. This method both gives the birds some worthwhile food and helps to keep them out of mischief.

Mixed grain
There are of course other types of food available, all of which can play an important part in the birds' welfare. Ideally, if they are fed a dampened mash in the morning, they should be given mixed grain at night. It can be purchased from your local grain merchant. Some of the ingredients the birds will pick out and eat right away, and others will sometimes be left. If this mixed grain – in Canada it is referred to as 'scratch' – is given to the bantams just before dusk, they have a full crop before settling on their perches. Some fanciers feed their birds mixed grain only – twice a day, every day – but this is not good practice. It is not the right diet to be given continually; it does fill their crops, but it does not have the protein and vitamins contained by layers' or breeders' mash.

Pellets
Another useful food for bantams are the small layers' or breeders' pellets, which are full of protein and specially manufactured for the purpose. Given at frequent intervals, they boost both your bantams' health and their egg-laying capabilities.

As time goes on, you will gain experience and find out exactly what is the best food for a particular breed of bantams, especially where game bantams are concerned. Further knowledge will be gained when you start to show your birds, because you will discover that certain breeds do better on particular sorts of foods than others.

Finally, you must always keep a watchful eye on the food troughs. This is not only to see that they are clean (they will need scrubbing regularly) but to check whether the birds are eating up. If it is found that food is regularly being left, then they are being given too much and the amount should be reduced.

Water

The supply of water should be given constant attention. Bantams must always have fresh clean water available, and the water fountain should be in an easily accessible position for them. As already stated, the fountain must be kept clean. It is advisable to place it on a couple of bricks in the run or the house, so that when the birds are scratching the dirt is not thrown into the well of the fountain, polluting the water.

Care and protection

If bantams are worth keeping, then they are worth looking after properly, and anyone not prepared to take some trouble should not contemplate taking up this hobby. Far too often, a considerable amount of money is laid out on good-quality cabins with all the necessary fittings, and then when the novelty wears off the birds are left more or less to fend for themselves, and suffer from neglect.

Consistent care is necessary to ensure that the birds are basically comfortable and protected from the regular problems. For instance, all poultry houses at some time or other have unwelcome visitors in the form of red mite and lice. It is this sort of thing, as well as food, water and cleanliness, that should be constantly checked; if not, the birds' health will suffer.

Red mite and lice

The most usual place to find red mite is on the perches where they breed, crawling on to the birds during the night. They can play havoc if they occur in large numbers (as can lice), and the birds must be protected. Red mites, which suck the blood of the bird, are normally found round the vent. Lice too tend to congregate at the root of the feathers in this area. Both these parasites can also be found under the wings. The bantams should therefore be dusted or sprayed regularly with a suitable aerosol to keep them immune from attack. It is worth noting that when new stock is brought into the flock, or when birds are returned from a show, they should be given a quick spray in case they have brought mites with them.

Some fanciers use a specially prepared egg (this can be purchased from a corn merchant) which is placed in the nest. When a bird enters the nest to lay its egg, it comes in contact with the special egg, which is impregnated with insecticide to kill any mites the bird might be carrying. These impregnated eggs work perfectly well but are not the whole answer, as male birds, and any females which are not laying and therefore don't use the nest, remain untreated.

The best time to spray the birds is when they are on the perch; at the same time give the perch a quick burst of spray, especially at either end, where the wood fits into the bracket supports. This is definitely a place where mites are likely to lodge.

Wind and sun

The effects of wind and sun on your birds need attention, particularly when bantams with large lobes (such as Minorcas or Rosecombs) are kept. Once the lobes become blistered, this can be an ongoing problem, particularly in show birds. Fanciers showing these breeds are very much aware of this and do not allow their birds to be exposed. They are either kept inside or protected from wind and sun by runs which have 2ft high protective corrugated sheeting all the way round. If they are in movable runs, then these will often have a piece of wood placed along the top to provide shade.

Winter protection

In winter you need to pay more attention to your birds. A daily check to see that the water in the fountain is not frozen is a first essential. And you will need to take great care when letting birds out in the snow for the first time: if they have never seen snow before, they can suddenly become very flighty, and this of course can be disturbing. If there is no reason to let them out and their premises are large enough, then they are better indoors when deep snow is on the ground. However, there must be plenty of litter in the cabin, and it is a good idea to feed them with dry mash from a hopper, so that they have to peck at it much longer in order to satisfy themselves. This keeps them out of trouble, as do a few handfuls of mixed grain thrown into the litter – the birds have to scratch for it to get satisfaction. They do not then get bored and start such mischief as egg eating and feather pecking.

You should be particularly careful to collect all the eggs daily, because a severe frost can crack the shells.

As already mentioned, during times of severe frost the combs of male birds, particularly those of Leghorns and Minorcas, and the spikes of some of the Rosecombed breeds, must be checked for frostbite.

Care and attention are what make a good stockman. Whilst there are daily and routine jobs to be done with breeding bantams, it is the fancier who pays that extra little bit of attention and instantly recognises problems who is the successful one.

Cleanliness

The heading care and protection must of course include cleanliness. It is essential that the nest boxes are kept filled with good clean straw or hay; if not, eggs laid on the base of the nest box could crack, and this would encourage egg eating. Nest boxes allowed to become dirty can harbour such pests as fleas. Cleanliness is indeed a priority and something that you should always have in mind. The best way of ensuring the prevention of any disease is to keep the cabins (including the nest boxes) and the runs clean and tidy.

It is recommended that you clean out the cabins once a week, but this does not mean thoroughly disinfecting the premises each time. The dropping boards should be cleaned weekly and fresh sawdust scattered on them; check the litter and remove any damp areas. At the same time look at the food troughs and drinking fountains and clean where necessary. Check and clean the perches.

After cleaning out the cabin, it is important that the manure is not simply tipped into a corner of the bantam run. This does happen and is a dreadful practice, merely encouraging disease. Take the waste away and put it in a specially prepared heap, well out of the way of the bantams.

As previously mentioned, the addition of a little lime to the litter when cleaning out is a good idea: it has the double effect of killing off unwanted parasites and sweetening the litter. It should not of course be overdone.

Providing the above cleanliness routine is followed, all should be well. A thorough cleaning operation should take place annually, as it does in one's own home – a good springclean after the winter months. It is at this time that a maintenance check should be made. One of the first places to be inspected is the roof, to ensure that the felt has not become torn during the winter gales and made a way for water to reach the roof. It is important too to check that the windows will open as they should, now that warmer weather is coming. This is the time to paint the cabin with creosote – which helps to preserve the wood and is another deterrent to those parasites that have the habit of lodging in all the nooks and crannies. Needless to say, it is advisable not to have birds in the cabin when creosoting and for a few days after until all the fumes have gone.

Your properly constructed bantam unit with its residents properly fed, cared for and protected will give you much pleasure.

4
Breeding and Rearing

There will come a time, probably sooner rather than later, when you wish to start breeding from your stock. You will probably have discussed this with various fanciers in your area, as well as with members of your local poultry club. Having received much advice but having no practical experience, your mind may be a jumble of information. Indeed advice from one fancier could well contradict that from another. However, no matter which breed of bantam is kept, certain basic rules must be followed.

The putting together of the breeding pen, the group of specially chosen bantams that you believe are capable of producing ideal stock, is one of the most important jobs of the whole year. Ill-considered decisions can easily and rapidly produce the wrong sort of future stock with its attendant disappointments. You must be perfectly clear as to what exactly you wish to breed: what are you trying to achieve? This point must especially be borne in mind when breeding for exhibition purposes.

The breeding pen

For the breeding pen you need one male and 4–6 females. Look at your stock. 'Type' is the first essential in any breed. No matter how well marked the bird may be or how perfect in other ways, if it is the wrong 'type' – does not have the carriage, deportment and shape required by the standards for its breed – then it is wrong for the breeding pen. It is no use breeding from birds which have long backs if the aim is to produce a bird of jaunty appearance. Birds in the breeding pen must excel in the various points that they are to reproduce and the dominant points must be clearly visible.

It is essential that only healthy stock is used and birds which conform to the standard. For instance, birds that are possibly duck-footed or with the incorrect leg colour or wry tails or roach backs should never be considered. Birds with such deformities are unfit for breeding purposes – all sorts of problems would occur in the resultant stock. Also your birds must have the correct combs, particularly in breeds where head points are important. Eye colour, too, must be absolutely right, while those breeds where lobes play an important part must excel in this feature and have lobes of good substance. Shape is another important point, especially in hard-feather bantams.

Besides these basic and fundamental principles, if you are breeding birds where markings are very important you must give extra thought to the making up of your breeding pen. Again your aims must be borne in mind. It is particularly important that the birds to be used not only have the colour and definition of markings required for their breed but have them so strongly that the breeding pen must be capable of reproducing them correctly. One method which has often been tried (and more often than not has failed) is to go to a show and buy a male bird from one fancier and females from several others. It has been known for a beginner to buy a winning cock and a winning hen in the belief that within twelve months show birds of the correct standards will be produced. Unfortunately it just does not work that way. If a bird does not show the characteristics of its particular breed very strongly, then it should not be considered for the breeding pen – unless of course, the fancier knows his stock extremely well (the blood line, the earlier generations), in which case a particular bird may possibly be considered to have latent advantages.

At the time of making up your breeding pen, it is never a bad thing to visit the breeder from whom your birds were purchased. Not only can sound advice be obtained on your particular breed, but you will be able to see at first hand the birds that he is using and to note relevant points.

The belief of some fanciers that good show birds can only be bred from one cock and one hen, so that is all that should be in the breeding pen, is not entirely valid. There is certainly no harm in specialising, and even specialising in double mating (which is a more detailed subject); but for now, the points already mentioned will get the beginner well on the way to success.

Fertility

There are one or two points concerning fertility which should be noted. The virility of the male bird is of course vital: if he is not fertile, then much time and effort is wasted. The age of the breeding pen too should be taken into consideration. Generally speaking, males over the age of four years should not be used, although an exception is often made for a good cock that has a proven record, especially in breeding show birds. In contrast, it is an established practice that females are not used until they are two years old; it is considered that pullets do not have sufficient substance for the breeding pen.

It is important that the birds are comfortable. Before the breeding pen is put together, the birds should be sprayed to ensure that they are free from lice and mite. The male bird should not have sharp spurs – if he has, the hens will simply keep out of his way! If the spurs have to be trimmed, then exercise great care. Snip off about a quarter of the spur with a sharp pair of pliers, and rub down the end with sandpaper so that it is smooth and will not cut the female when mating takes place. Also to improve fertility, experienced fanciers often clip the feathers around the vents of the females.

It is extremely important that the breeding pen is fertile, so it must be stressed again and again that only fit and healthy birds, birds that are true to type, have the strong points and characteristics of their particular breed, and are capable of reproducing them, should be used.

Hatching eggs

People wanting to breed chickens for the very first time often think that all the eggs should be left in the nest, and eventually one of the hens from the breeding pen will sit on them. Nothing could be further from the truth.

The care of hatching eggs is important. From them will come – it is hoped – the birds for next year's stock, and from them will descend future generations. The nests in which eggs for hatching are laid must be clean and, as mentioned before, be lined with straw or hay for the birds' comfort when laying. Then the eggs should be carefully collected and checked to ensure that they do not have any cracks and that the shells are of good substance. They should be stored on the normal-size traditional egg-tray, with the narrow end downwards, at room temperature. It is wrong to store the eggs in warm places or in cold cellars, and it is equally wrong just to put them on some ledge where they can roll about.

A white Silkie hen (often referred to as a bantam but categorised as standard bred) sitting on eggs. This method will work but is not ideal

An egg-tray is the correct place for them, and they should ideally be turned once a day before incubation. (Eggs stored in this manner can be kept for a maximum of 14 days.)

Hatching eggs should not be collected as soon as the breeding pen is mated up, because the first few that are laid will almost certainly be infertile. At least ten days should elapse before the first eggs are collected. If you are breeding exhibition stock and for some reason or other the male bird is changed during the breeding season, the ten-day waiting period *must* be observed. If very selective breeding is being carried out, then there is no harm in marking the eggs with a pencil to show which particular breeding pen they have been collected from, or – if several breeds are kept – which breed has laid them.

Obviously the fresher the eggs for incubation, the better the chances of hatching, providing they are fertile; however, if the simple method which has been described is followed, then success should be achieved.

Having considered the care of hatching eggs, you will now need to decide the method of incubation. There are two choices – broody hens or incubators, and both methods have proven success.

Incubation – with a broody hen

The oldest and the traditional way of hatching bantam eggs is to use a broody hen, a method that has been successful for breeders over many years.

Bantams or standard-bred hens become broody by nature. When a hen has laid a batch of eggs, she may (not always, by any means) become broody; furthermore, broodiness is often brought on by warm weather. A method of encouraging bantams nearing the end of their laying cycle to become broody is to leave some eggs in the nest – to tempt them to sit. It is rare that bantams become broody during the winter, but if you should find a broody hen during this time then do everything to encourage her. Eggs hatched during the very early part of the year produce what is known as 'early chickens', and these can be extremely useful if you wish to exhibit at some of the midsummer shows.

Some breeds are more prone to broodiness than others; generally speaking it is the heavier breeds that produce the ultimate broody bantam. However, most experienced fanciers use what is known as a Silkie cross. A Silkie, though often referred to as a bantam, is a standard-bred fowl. When it is crossed with a Sussex or a Wyandotte, or a similar breed of bantam, the resulting females make excellent mothers. Most fanciers use Silkie cross Sussex, the progeny of a Silkie cock mated to a Sussex hen.

Before a broody hen is used there are a few matters to deal with. First you have to decide where she is going to sit on her batch of eggs. Then you prepare the nest and check that she will be secure, because she will be sitting for twenty-one days with only brief daily respites when she is let off the eggs to get food and water.

It is perfectly true that many bantam fanciers just put two or three orange boxes in the corner of a cabin, line them with straw, place the eggs inside and set the broody on them. It is also true that chicks do hatch successfully this way. But again there is a correct – more reliably successful – way of dealing with broody hens. Undoubtedly the ideal way is to make a 'broody box', as shown on page 39. The emphasis is on the structure of the base of the box. It should be well felted, with a hinged lid, and air holes for ventilation. Ideally it should also have a sloping roof. The bottom of the box must not have any boards whatsoever – just a good covering of strong wire mesh. This is not just to prevent vermin entering the box, but to ensure that the broody hen is sitting as near to mother earth as possible: in other words, nature at its best. The box must be placed in a safe position where it is not likely to get knocked or blown over. The inside should be lined with straw in the shape of a basin, making a comfortable nest for the hen to sit in. During the three-week period that she covers the eggs she will be drawing natural moisture from the ground on to the porous egg shells and this helps enormously at hatching time: the chicks hatch much easier than when they have to cope with tough shells and dried skins, so the risk of losing them is drastically reduced.

Having shaped the nest, it is a good idea to put some pot (false) eggs in it, three or four, and to place the broody on them for a couple of days to get her used to the nest and you satisfied that she has settled. Before putting her on the nest, spray or dust her vent

Outdoor box for broody bantams. Each section has air holes and the nests are set in the earth

to ensure that there are no mites or lice; otherwise, if they are present, at the end of the three-week period they will have multiplied into hundreds. Once the bird has settled the false eggs can be taken away and the hatching eggs placed under her. There are no hard and fast rules as to how many eggs a broody bantam will take – it really depends on her size – but it can be safely assumed that she will look after nine or ten eggs quite comfortably.

During her sitting period, the broody hen must be taken from the nest every day for feeding. Simply take her to the nearest empty cabin where corn and fresh water are available and after about fifteen minutes, when she has filled her crop, she will be ready to go back on the nest. It is at this time that care must be taken that she does not break any of the eggs.

Broodies can be let off for feeding at any time of day, but the usual practice is to take them off in the evening, when you will probably have more time. Also they tend to re-settle that little bit quicker as nightfall approaches.

Testing the eggs

The excitement of breeding, especially when hatching eggs for the first time, builds up about the fourteenth day. Now the eggs can be tested, known as 'candling', to see if they contain chicks. This exercise can only be done at night to achieve absolutely true results. It is a most reliable method which has been used for generations. You take the eggs one at a time from underneath the broody hen and hold them between your index finger and thumb. By shining a torch beam underneath and through the shell it can be established whether the egg contains an embryo or not. Eggs that are completely clear are infertile. Those which contain chicks show a huge dark patch with just a small clear space in the thick end of the egg, which is the air space. Remove infertile eggs, and leave the broody hen to sit for the next seven days on eggs which definitely contain chicks. Don't count those chickens before they are hatched, however, because things can still go wrong!

Hatching time

When dealing with broody hens it is the first few days (which have already been described) and the last few days which are important. The last few days are those which really ensure success or disappointment for the breeder. You can assist the process at this time, though there is no way to make quite certain that all the fertile eggs will hatch.

Three or four days before the chicks are due to hatch, when the broody is off her nest, splash the eggs with warm water. This will have a twofold effect. First it will soften the inside skin and the shells of the eggs, and most importantly the water will run off the eggs on to the nest and keep it moist. Secondly, it will stop the eggs from baking and the shells becoming hard, so that the chicks will hatch more easily on the 20th/21st day.

By employing these methods you should achieve success, but it must be pointed out that there will be the odd chick that is unable to get out of its shell. As when breeding any livestock, there is always the odd weak one. Many breeders believe that if a chick cannot get out of the shell of its own accord, then you shouldn't be bothered with it because it is probably a weakling anyway.

Having read how to hatch bantam chicks in the ideal way, in a broody box close to the earth, you will realise the benefits, as compared with using an old orange box in the corner of a cabin. But there are certain disadvantages as against using an incubator. There is the initial chore of making up the nest; but the biggest risk is the possibility of the broody hen 'coming off her nest'. Sometimes the hen just gives up being broody and wants to return to her normal life in the bantam pen. This situation can arise at any time during the incubation period, and you must be very quick to spot it and replace her immediately with another broody. Another disadvantage is that the hen has to be let off the eggs once a day on each of the 20 to 21 consecutive days of sitting time, with the attendant risk that she might break some each time she is put back. Generally speaking however, this is a successful method which will continue to be used.

Incubators

The alternative method of hatching bantam chickens is to use an incubator. These come in various sizes and sorts, both modern types and old traditional types. They occupy various price brackets too. Bantam breeders tend to use the smaller incubator, the 30-egg or the 60-egg size. If you decide to use an incubator, then you will be wise to invest in a new one and to follow the manufacturer's instructions rigidly.

The advantages of using an incubator are that there probably isn't as much work involved as when using a broody hen, and you have the pleasure of seeing the chicks hatch. However, there are disadvantages. The incubator must be kept somewhere with an electricity supply – most incubators are electrically warmed nowadays – and not everyone has enough room in the garage for it to be safe there. So it is not always housed in the most convenient place. Then it is terribly important that the temperature and moisture content are controlled correctly, otherwise the eggs will simply bake and the whole operation will fail. It is also necessary to turn the eggs over twice a day, unless the incubator is an automatic model. This equates with the shuffle performed by the broody hen as she turns round on her nest, turning her eggs in the process. So if you have to be absent for a period of time, you must arrange for someone else to turn the eggs and check the temperatures. Cost has to be taken into account, too; broody hens need feeding for 365 days of the year, of course, but there is not only a capital investment in the incubator but also the cost of the electricity (or occasionally oil) to run it.

Custom hatching

This is a method which is used by bantam breeders who have a commercial hatchery in their own village or nearby. You take the eggs to a commercial poultryman (who runs massive incubators) and they are placed alongside the thousands of other eggs.

Two important points must be borne in mind if using this method. First, your eggs must be clearly marked so that the poultryman knows exactly which eggs are whose. Secondly, the chickens must be collected on time and brought to their new surroundings in a suitable container. A traditional cardboard chicken box can be bought for the purpose; alternatively, a good strong box lined with some clean hay to keep the chickens warm can be used. The financial arrangements for this possibly least-used method are entirely between the breeder and the hatchery.

Rearing methods

During the three weeks of incubation you should decide on the chicks' home. There is a choice of three methods.

First, they can be taken with the mother broody to a new home; secondly, they can be reared under a brooder; thirdly, they can be reared with the aid of infra-red lamps. All three methods have proved successful, but for the bantam breeder it is strongly suggested that the first method is chosen. The brooder is sometimes used by bantam breeders who hatch large numbers of chicks, and for them it is ideal. However, for the breeder with four or five hatches at different times of year, the broody-hen method is ideal. The infra-red method is reliable providing that the electricity supply is not cut off and the lamp is set correctly – but again it is more expensive than the traditional broody-hen method.

Rearing with a broody hen

If you are going to allow your broody hen to rear her chicks, the first principle to bear in mind is that their first home (which they will occupy for the first two or three weeks of their life) must be as comfortable as you can make it. The main object during this period is to get the chicks going and nothing must be allowed to hinder or prevent this. Again, of course broody hens have reared their chicks under all sorts of less than ideal conditions – in old tea chests, behind old tin sheets, and probably even in old baths – but if you are taking the trouble to breed your birds it is worth doing everything possible to increase the chances of success.

What is required is a run, some 4ft in length by 15 to 18in in width, where the broody bantam and her young can (and should) be completely separated from the rest of the flock. If you are planning to rear several batches of chicks during a season, you may well have areas specially partitioned off under the dropping boards of a cabin, or have a small shed suitably divided. Both places are ideal, whether permanent or otherwise. If temporary runs are to be made, then there is nothing more useful than breeze blocks which can be adjusted to make runs of the required size. If this method is used, a good tip is to line the floor with paper bags (this provides extra warmth for the new arrivals) and build the breeze blocks on top. Lay frames covered with wire netting over the blocks. If special partitions are built under dropping boards, then a door made with wire-netting mesh is necessary. It is advisable for the floor to be of wood, to provide warmth, and of course clean litter must be used: wood chippings or small shavings are the best type, because chicks tend to peck at sawdust and will occasionally eat it, which does them no good at all.

You will need to provide the broody hen and her flock with a supply of clean fresh water, from a traditional fountain. For the food, many fanciers use a small metal trough, but from experience I recommend using a traditional egg tray for the first two or three weeks. The reason for this is that chickens like to hear themselves pecking, and they can peck away at the food in the cardboard slots all day long without damaging their beaks. Furthermore, the food in the slots of the tray cannot be scratched out and this does prevent wastage. When soiled, the trays can be replaced by clean ones.

Rearing by a brooder

When rearing chicks the first thing to guard against is draughts – this is particularly important where you are using a brooder heated by an oil lamp. Whilst all the other rules of chick-rearing apply – have a well-ventilated building with plenty of light and free from disease – you must be aware of the fire risks involved in using a brooder lamp; great control and attention is necessary. The brooder lamp is often put in a corner of a large wooden building where other stock is kept; but this is inadvisable, for should the lamp catch fire not only will you lose your chicks but the whole cabin could be set alight, with the loss of all the other stock in it. The best advice is to set up your brooder lamp in a completely separate building, away from all other stock; if possible in a brick building, although these can be somewhat cold.

Light the lamp at least forty-eight hours before putting the chicks under the brooder. This is not only to generate warmth ready for the arrival of the day-old chicks but also to ensure that the lamp is functioning correctly and that there are no unforseen draughts in the building. Remove any paper, sacks or other inflammable items from the vicinity, and see that fire precautions are of the highest standard.

For the first few days in the chicks' life under a brooder they will not venture from beneath it very much. Place the metal feed troughs (use these rather than the egg trays recommended for chicks with a broody hen, because of the fire risk) at strategic points where the chicks can feed whilst still feeling the warmth from the lamp. At this stage it is necessary to control their ventures, so erect a six-inch high wall (of either concrete blocks or metal) all round the brooder. As the chicks grow, the enclosed area can be gradually extended until the barrier is taken completely away in order to give them the full run of the cabin or building in which they are being reared.

About the third or fourth week you will notice that the chicks are starting to feather well, and providing the weather is warm you can turn down the brooder lamp gradually, until you eventually put it out. Turn off the lamp for a short period during the day at first, lengthening the time steadily until you have dispensed with it entirely.

This method of rearing chicks has been practised successfully for many years, but remember that the brooder lamp must be checked constantly to see that it is working properly and that it contains sufficient oil. It is definitely not the method to use if you intend to go away for a long weekend and leave the care of the chicks to your next-door neighbour.

Rearing by infra-red

Another successful and reliable method (barring power cuts) is to rear your chickens under an infra-red lamp; it is the easiest method, once the lamp is set up, though probably more expensive. Again the basic principles must be followed as far as cleanliness and draughts are concerned. Switch on the lamp some twenty-four hours before placing the chicks under it.

As with a brooder, you need to erect a metal surround or small wall of concrete blocks to keep the chicks (certainly for the first ten days) in a reasonably confined space. Hang the lamp over the centre of this area some 9in from the ground; as the chickens grow, gradually raise it. For instance, at the end of the first week you could raise it by say an inch, then increase the distance at intervals as necessary. As with the brooder, about the third or fourth week switch off the lamp for a short period during the day, steadily lengthening the time until you finally dispense with the lamp.

Whilst some bantam fanciers will find the infra-red lamp a convenient chick-rearing method, it is not recommended for the breeder who wishes to raise five or six batches of chickens per annum because of the expense involved. However, if you decide this is the rearing system for you, here is a word of caution. If the lamp is positioned too low the toes of the chicks will tend to turn inwards; this fault *may* right itself when the chicks eventually get outside on to fresh land, but it does not always work out that way.

Storing your rearing equipment
Whichever method you choose, when you have finished with the equipment you must thoroughly disinfect and clean it before storing it away. Far too often good equipment is left to stand in a corner of the building until the following year when it is needed again; then there may not be sufficient time to do any necessary repairs. If put away in good condition, the equipment will have many more years of life.

Rearing tactics

You are most likely to choose a broody bantam to rear your chicks, and on this presumption I recommend that you move them to their new quarters at night. There are many methods for moving chicks from the nest to their new home, and providing the broody is reliable there should not be much difficulty providing you are patient. The favourite way is to carry the chicks in a hay-lined cardboard box (take the broody hen with you as well). Take out two or three chicks and place them in the corner of their new home. Carefully introduce the broody to her chicks; she should gradually settle in the corner with the young nestled beneath her. You can now place the remaining chicks under the broody, one by one.

As mentioned earlier, the cross-bred Silkies or heavy breed of bantams are recommended for rearing chicks. They are far less flighty than other breeds and once such a bird has proved to be a reliable mother she is worth her weight in gold. There is nothing worse than moving chicks late at night only to find that the broody hen, having sat so patiently for three weeks, totally refuses to have anything to do with them. This does not often occur but it is infuriating when it does.

If there are two or three batches of chicks being hatched and reared at the same time it is a good idea, if practicable, to mix them. For instance, if you have three broodies and one has hatched black chickens, the second white chickens and the third yellow chickens, then mix up the colours and divide them among the broody hens. Should something happen to one of the hens, then you can place her chicks with the other two. Otherwise if, say, the broody rearing all the white chicks suddenly died, the other two mothers certainly would not take white chicks, after being used to solely yellow or black. (This is not to say that if a particular bantam has reared black chicks one year she will rear only black chicks in subsequent years – that of course is not true.)

You may wish to rear your chicks outside from the day they are hatched, by using a chick coop and movable run. This is a good practice and one which has been proved very successful. However, for the beginner who is rearing chicks for the first time, the old slogan 'better safe than sorry' is probably the right approach. Moving to coop and runs is a logical step to take when you have gained some experience.

When you have moved your chicks to their new home, you should thoroughly clean and disinfect the area they have vacated so that it is ready for the next arrivals.

Feeding the new chicks

There are various foods available for chicks, especially chick mash, but from experience the best first food is chick crumbs. In the first couple of weeks, if you feed chick mash there can be some wastage, especially if the broody hen is boisterous and scratches it all over the place. Also it takes the chicks much longer to fill their crops with mash, and whilst that is beneficial when they are older they are of course too young to damage each other from boredom at a few days old. Crumbs are a most satisfying wholesome food and very beneficial to a young chick's health.

You can continue to feed chick crumbs until the birds have been moved to their next home – at about three or four weeks old, depending on how they have developed and how well feathered they have become. Whatever happens, after you have introduced them to their next home they should be fed on chick crumbs until they have settled in. It would be wrong to change the surroundings and the food all at the same time; it should be done gradually.

Once they have settled and are fast becoming growers, then growers' mash should be introduced at the morning feed, at the rate of 25 per cent, the remaining 75 per cent being comprised of chick crumbs. Gradually a half-and-half situation will arise, then the balance will be in favour of mash until the chick crumbs are completely withdrawn and the diet will be entirely of growers' mash. It is recommended that the mash is fed in a dampened form. As the birds get older some mixed grain can be given in the evening, simply to fill up their crops.

Moving outside

When the chicks are some three to four weeks old and are about to be moved outside it is the time when the disease coccidiosis can strike. If you discover traces of blood in the droppings, and the chicks themselves are looking miserable, with their wings drooping, you should immediately consult your veterinary surgeon. Coccidiosis can prove to be fatal and it is essential that treatment is given on first sight. In fact when the chicks reach this age, many breeders give them a dose of the medicine normally used to treat the disease simply as a preventative measure.

Choice of unit

There are several types of unit, equally good, from which to choose the chicks' first outside home. You could use a section of a cabin which has been specially segregated, with an outside run, or you may have hay boxes or fold units available. All these serve the purpose adequately.

If using a segregated area in a poultry cabin, it is important (as with a hay box or fold unit) that the broody hen accompanies the chicks to their first outside home and stays with them for a further few weeks. It will soon become obvious when the chicks can manage without their broody mother, because they will tend to become well feathered and will spend less and less time with her, particularly at night, when they will sleep adjacent to her rather than under her.

Hay box/fold unit

Hay boxes are somewhat similar to fold units. They are movable houses with a run and sleeping quarters attached. The only real difference is that the hay box has hay or straw pushed under the roof to give additional warmth. These units have proved most successful over the years and have the advantage that they can be

Hay-box brooder, a useful run for rearing chickens

moved to fresh ground every three or four days. It is essential to ensure that they are vermin-proof; one tip is to run a strand of barbed wire around the bottom of the unit about a couple of inches from the floor to stop foxes or a neighbour's dog trying to burrow underneath.

Chicks reared in these units usually grow extremely well, but you need to exercise close vigilance for the first two or three days after they are moved in. The broody, having reared chicks by this method before, may at dusk go through the pop hole into the sleeping accommodation, leaving the chicks behind. Alternatively, if the chicks are reluctant at first to go in from the run through the little pop hole, then the broody may snuggle down in a corner of the run with them; this is risky as there could be bad weather during the night. After a few nights both the broody bantam and her batch will have become used to going in and out of the sleeping accommodation and all will be well. Chicks reared under a broody bantam can be transferred to a hay box or fold unit a little earlier than those reared under an infra-red or brooder, because they still have their broody mother to provide protection and warmth.

When the time comes to take the broody hen away, you should spray or dust her to deter lice or mites and check that there are no signs of scaly leg – a little sulphur ointment rubbed on her legs at this stage will ensure that she is kept clear of it.

You can keep your young bantams in fold units or hay boxes for a considerable time. Several experienced fanciers, with four or five fold units full of bantam chicks, keep them there until they are three or four months old, managing them very carefully. Besides watching for coccidiosis, it is necessary to look out for signs of feather pecking. This generally breaks out through boredom and can be caused through not regularly moving the runs on to new ground where the bantam chicks can scratch happily with plenty to interest them. If left on soiled turf, not only feather pecking but other troubles are more likely.

Third and final move

Ideally this will be to a large cabin, with spacious scratching facilities and the comfort of a perch. Whilst it is inadvisable to allow growing bantams to perch at too early an age, because of the possibility that they may develop crooked breastbones, they can do so after approximately four months, when their breastbones will have virtually developed.

You will need to bear in mind that the birds are now growing quickly and will need more space at the feeding trough. Whereas one trough would do for them at possibly eight weeks of age, at five months they may need two or even three, and probably an extra water fountain as well. Cockerels and pullets of most breeds will live together usually very happily at five to six months of age, but if a cockerel is pulled out for a short period (even just two or three days) it is inadvisable to put it back in the flock, because fighting could well occur.

Examining your own young stock

The final stage is perhaps the most exciting and rewarding one for the breeder. Your enthusiasm was great at the sight of your first chicks, but it is only after six months' careful and attentive work that you know the result. It is now that you should feel a great deal of satisfaction as you settle down to examine your stock by lengthy, patient and detailed observation, to establish whether your aim has been reached.

Some cockerels now tend to become somewhat exuberant, with the consequence that they spoil some of the feathers of the pullets. Start the separation process – segregating the cockerels from the pullets, and then the good ones from the poor ones of both sexes.

The first exercise is to spend some time quietly sitting in a corner of the cabin, simply observing the birds. You will be looking for such things as twisted toes and wry tails (see Glossary), and any birds having these faults should be immediately taken out and put elsewhere.

The second exercise should be done at night. Handle and thoroughly examine each bird – if this is done at night it can be carried out quietly without birds flying all over the place with resultant damage and possible breaking of sickle feathers in the cockerels. Taking each bird, systematically examine it to ensure that its beak is not twisted, the eye colour is as laid down in the breed standards and the eye not faulty. The comb should be the correct shape; if the bird has a rosecomb the comb should be straight and not lop-sided, with the leader not only of the right shape but also in the correct position. Birds with single combs should be examined likewise to ensure that the serrations are correct, and that the comb is in the right position. As you handle the bird, check the body to ascertain that it does not have a roach back and that the breastbone is straight. Do a brief check of the legs and feet to see that no toenails are missing and the colour is correct. Your check for physical defects is now complete, and no doubt you will have thinned out your birds, those failing the test being put elsewhere certainly for the time being.

The third stage will involve you in a more thorough examination of the birds in order to compare them with the standard laid down for the breed. The breed clubs lay down the various standards in conjunction with the Poultry Club of Great Britain and you will need to be fully conversant with them. In some cases the third check can be made at night, whilst in others it must be done in daylight. This particularly applies to those breeds where colour is so important (such as Rhode Island Red bantams), for it is only by carefully examining them in good daylight that a true assessment can be reached. Other breeds are heavily pointed on markings and others on shape; therefore it is important that you have sufficient knowledge of what is good or otherwise in order to carry out this part of the exercise.

There is no doubt that by now you will have thinned out your birds even further. You have removed those with the wrong colour, shape and markings and also any birds that are either too big or too small. It is possible that you will have put a very high percentage of your birds on one side for disposal. But in spite of this you should still feel highly rewarded because those left in the pen are a credit to your breeding and are of great potential in the show pen.

Normally this is where the sorting-out programme ends, but there are some breeders who take it one stage further and probably rightly. At this fourth stage the cockerels which have been selected as good examples of the breed, and which are to be kept, are placed one in each show pen so that the breeder can quietly assess for an hour or two how they look in the pen. More often than not no changes will be made, but there is the odd occasion when a bird which has passed the original test may for some reason or other be rejected. The test is then repeated with the pullets.

After the whole sorting-out exercise has been completed, it is a sound idea to put a ring on each bird that has come out with honours and is not therefore for sale. This means that when someone calls wanting to buy birds, those for sale are instantly recognisable. However, a word of warning – if you decide to put all the cockerels back together, then do not keep them out of their pen for too long. As mentioned earlier, in most breeds cockerels which have been brought up together will live happily for a considerable period of time without fighting, but if one or two are taken out temporarily they must be put back quickly, otherwise battle will commence. This then becomes a problem, because they will have to be separated for their own protection. The sooner these birds which are not wanted are sold, the better it is for those that are to remain.

Feeding point-of-lay pullets

Your young bantams will live on quite happily and healthily eating growers' mash and mixed corn until, around the age of six months, they are ready for laying. At this stage the food should be changed to a recommended layers' mash. Again, as when changing from chick mash to growers' mash, the change to the new food should be gradual. Providing it is done this way the birds will come to no harm.

Should you be keeping bantams mainly for the eggs they produce, then the pullets should be kept relatively quiet as they start laying. There is nothing worse than the next-door neighbour's dog or cat bounding into the cabin or poultry pen, causing the birds to panic. If this happens it will knock them off laying and some days could elapse before they recommence. The eggs for the first few weeks will be small but will gradually increase in size until they reach normal size. Occasionally soft-shelled eggs will be found – eggs whose shells have not been properly formed. It is always assumed that this is because the birds have not had sufficient grit, but whilst a few handfuls of it will assist, the general cause is over-production.

Some bantams lay better than others, ornamental breeds generally laying fewer eggs than do many of the heavy or light breeds. Again there are bantams that will lay for most of the year, whilst others lay predominantly during the spring and summer. For further details of the laying capabilities of some of the popular breeds, see pages 82–3.

5
Showing – The Challenge

It is probably a safe bet that if you have not accepted the challenge of showing up to this stage, then as you look at your current year's successful breeding you will be much encouraged to do so. The birds will be in excellent condition and at the peak of their form and you will probably hear such comments as 'fit to win at any show'.

There have been many books written on the subject of showing. Unfortunately, for one reason or another, advice offered is sometimes ignored, with resultant disappointment and possibly the loss of an exhibitor. The question is why? It is perhaps useful at this stage to make some observations on showing in general, the reasons for disappointments and the secrets of success. For the moment we will consider disappointments, but if the advice contained in the next few pages is followed, then such disappointments shouldn't occur.

Before you start exhibiting, that first principle must be observed – 'walk before you run'. All too frequently breeders have wanted to reach the top of the ladder before they have even started to climb it. Some can recite the breed standard, chapter and verse, but entirely lack practical experience. There are fanciers who have bought birds that have won at shows one week but fail to get in the first three places a fortnight later. There are breeders who have had substantial help from experienced neighbours in selecting and preparing show birds and yet still don't win. Most of all, there are breeders (if they can call themselves breeders) who have bought birds, often unseen, for big money, and still cannot reach their goal. Why? They haven't observed the first principle – walk before you run, be prepared to listen and learn, and above all realise that the show pen is the shop window for your stock. It is essential that this is realised; only stock which is true to standard, true to form, healthy and fit, of the right type, and properly prepared for showing, should ever be put in this show-pen shop window.

This advice may seem somewhat harsh but it is absolutely true.

Modern Game bantam cock – a showman's breed

You simply cannot just take your birds from their perches at night, put them into a basket, take them along to a show and expect to win. It has never worked that way and it never will. Showing is all about pride and presentation. Whether showing shire horses, Shetland ponies, white mice or bantams, it is the same principle – they must be shown properly (ie correctly) and to their best advantage. Digressing from the miniature bantam to the shire horse might seem like going from the ridiculous to the sublime, but the comparison illustrates the point. How often have crowds thronged round the show ring when the brewers' shire horses are on parade pulling their drays? The brasses and harness shine and the horses show off their excellent bloom and fitness and are a credit to the grooms exhibiting them. It is exactly the same when showing bantams – your aim must be to impress, and especially to impress the judge, who after all is the most important person on show day. He has to be convinced that your bird is the best, and only by following the basic principles of show preparation will you ever achieve this goal.

It takes time to get the birds in peak condition and with this in mind the showing programme must be carefully planned. Even when the birds have reached prime fitness there are the final preparations to be dealt with immediately prior to the show. It does not happen in five minutes and the job must be done properly. It is a good idea to visit several shows before deciding to take the plunge; you will be able to observe at first hand what is involved in presenting show birds to the best advantage.

There are not as many 'team men' about these days as there used to be – people breeding and showing exhibition bantams for a living, touring the country with their exhibits, sometimes entering as many as forty birds at one show. But there are still sufficient exhibitors showing a good number of birds from whom the lesson of perfect preparation can be learnt. It should not happen, but quite often a new exhibitor showing only one or two birds will find that his exhibits are not as well prepared as those of the team men. Why? It can be put down to the experience that the team men have gained over many years; the new exhibitor does not know the finer points of show preparation. If you wish to build up a good stud of bantams, then you must set out to win prizes, otherwise potential buyers will not want to know. You will reap handsome dividends by showing your birds properly, as well as the reward of great personal satisfaction.

You, as a potential exhibitor, have really to serve an apprenticeship, and some apprenticeships take longer to serve than others. It depends on your ability to absorb knowledge and the amount of help given by fellow exhibitors. Generally speaking, the experienced fancier will be only too pleased to help the novice. As time goes on, you will glean numerous tips and snippets of sound advice – but of course there are many wonderful secrets of success that are never divulged.

You are starting on a whole new field of poultry keeping when you decide to enter the show world. It will certainly take up more of your time and this is a factor that should be given consideration. Not only will time have to be spent in conditioning and preparing your show birds, but you will be travelling to and from shows near and far. Then, you will need to erect show pens in a suitable small building on your premises – this is what is commonly referred to as a 'penning room'.

All these factors must be well considered before taking up the challenge of showing your bantams.

The penning room

It is often said that shows are won at home, and if this is true then the place where they are won is the fancier's penning room. It is something that you as an exhibitor simply cannot manage without.

The term 'penning room' could be translated to 'training room'. It is the area where you erect some pens, identical to those used at shows. It is a distinct advantage if the penning room is a separate building, but if this is not possible then it must be in a section of a cabin where the show birds can be separated, physically and visually, from the other stock. The reason why they should not be visible to the rest of the flock is that if cockerels are penned up and can see hens wandering about the penning room, then they are likely to become somewhat restless, with resultant damage to their feathers.

Show pens can be purchased ready-made. It is a sound idea to erect them in a double layer, exactly as seen at many of the shows (except that yours should be erected so that they are a permanent fixture on good sound timber). Thus you could have six cages on the bottom row with six cages above. If erected at a height of approximately 3ft 6in from the floor, you will have room underneath to store such things as show baskets etc. To complete the pens, divide them from each other by means of a wooden or metal partition. All that is needed now is a drinker for each pen

Ideal penning room

(exactly the same as those used at shows) and some good clean sawdust.

It is helpful if the penning room has electric light – then much of the work involved in training your birds can be done at night in your leisure time. Also, placed in a convenient position, you should have a cupboard where various medicines and sprays can be kept, as well as a food bin in which you can store any special nutritional supplements you intend to give your birds before shows. As you will be spending a great deal of time in the penning room, the final important item on the inventory is a comfortable seat on which you can relax quietly and observe your birds.

Besides being the training room, the penning room is also the fancier's showroom. More often than not, many of your best birds will be in the show cages and it will most likely be the first place to which you will take visitors. It is therefore very important that the site chosen should be in a suitable position. Being the showroom it must not be dark, dingy and tatty, but an advertisement, scrupulously clean, with plenty of light and shaded from the sun – otherwise on warm sunny days there will tend to be a greenhouse effect, damaging to the birds' health over a prolonged period. Also, birds tend to moult much quicker if exposed to continual heat for days on end. (This is the reason why birds on free range tend to seek shade on warm afternoons.)

The room and the pens should be cleaned out regularly – at least once a week and more frequently prior to a major show. Many fanciers who show 'White' breeds clean out their show pens every day prior to a big event, solely to ensure that the birds do not pick up any dirt or dust. If it is a showroom then it must give that impression.

However, the practical use of the penning room is, as already stated, as a training room. When the birds are first put in the show pens they will tend to be scared, nervous and flighty, and they must be calmed down before the show day. Birds which have not been trained correctly have no chance of winning a prize. All that happens is that when the judge puts his hand inside the show cage they fly round and round, showering him with sawdust. The effect and the judge's impression need no describing!

Training

The pre-show routine is to place the bantams in the pens two or three weeks beforehand, when they will quickly adapt to their new surroundings. At feeding times, put your hand into the pen to give them their food; they will gradually get used to the idea and accept the procedure without panic. (Then they will not be disturbed by the judge putting in his hand to pick them up.) Eventually, after a few days, the birds will settle down and become tame and will even start to peck the food from your hand. At this stage you are certainly on the road to success. All that remains to be done is to visit the penning room regularly at night and place your hand in the cage, quietly and patiently catch the bird, take it from the cage and look at it just as the judge at a show would do, and then return it. After several evenings' training in this sort of routine, the bird gets used to being taken from its pen and put back again.

The other lesson that must be taught is that of the training stick. Most judges carry a judging stick or training stick; these are used simply to turn the bird round so that the judge can see the shape or markings on the other side. It is a good idea to have a stick permanently hanging up in your penning room and to use it continually so that when the birds arrive at the show to be judged it is nothing new to them.

The washing of poultry for exhibition will shortly be described. Remember that it is essential that after washing and drying the bird should be returned to show pens that are meticulously clean, and this high standard of cleanliness must prevail throughout the remaining time to show day.

So the fancier's 'set-up' is now virtually complete. The stud, patiently built up over twelve months, contains breeding stock, the current year's breeding of cockerels and pullets (with, hopefully, show stock amongst them) and a penning room or a showroom. The long, hard but often exciting journey to shows, the challenge of the show world, is about to begin. But how?

Local show society

In most parts of the British Isles there is a local bantam show society which will have been in existence for many years, organised by enthusiastic fanciers in the area. These societies are run, as any other society, with their own organising committee and chairman, treasurer, secretary, and sometimes show manager specifically to look after any show the society might hold. Many of these organisations have their own premises, whilst others meet regularly in the local village pub and hold their shows in the local village hall or suitable premises nearby.

If you are contemplating showing your bantams you should contact the local society, become a member and get involved in what is going on. Many of the societies organise an annual programme which includes lectures and talks by experienced fanciers, often illustrated not only with slides but also by good and bad examples of the particular breed being described. It is from talks such as these, and particularly those relating to the breed in which you are interested, that most benefit will be derived. Demonstrations are often held and members' open discussion evenings. Sometimes a panel consisting of experienced fanciers from nearby areas will hold a question-and-answer time and this again will afford good sound knowledge. In addition to these activities, and from a completely different angle, the local society will hold members' social evenings where bantam fanciers get together in groups and the entire conversation is about bantams, all helping to make an interesting and enjoyable evening.

In the annual calendar of events of the local poultry society will be the dates of the various shows the particular society is to hold. There could well be two or three members' shows, which are restricted to members of that particular society – in other words, truly local shows. There may also be two or three open shows, in which fanciers from much further afield can compete against the local birds. These shows are notified well in advance and the new exhibitor must ensure that he has furnished the society secretary with his correct address in order to receive show schedules and entry forms.

Schedules – bantam classification

But what is a schedule and how should an entry form be completed? A schedule gives details of when and where a show is to be held, the members of the organising committee and the names of the judges. It gives details of the various entry fees and the prize money, dates when the entries close, and the various rules. The schedule contains the classification – all the various classes for the different breeds to be exhibited at that show, with any special prizes, rosettes and diplomas offered by breed clubs.

To give you an idea of the classification – which after all is the heart of the schedule and of most interest to any exhibitor – and the rules, here is a classification for bantams from one of the north-west of England's leading poultry shows – Ribble Valley Poultry Society. It is reproduced by kind permission of the organising committee of that society.

Class 1 Old English Game, Black Red Cock
Class 2 Old English Game, Clay or Wheaten Hen
Class 3 Old English Game, Spangle Cock
Class 4 Old English Game, Spangle Hen
Class 5 Black, Red or Spangled Cockerel
Class 6 Clay, Wheaten or Spangled Pullet
Class 7 Old English Game, Black or Blue, Cock
Class 8 Old English Game, Black or Blue, Hen
Class 9 Old English Game, Black or Blue, Cockerel or Pullet

Class 10 Old English Game, A.O.C. Cock
Class 11 Old English Game, A.O.C. Hen
Class 12 A.O.C. O.E.G. Cockerel
Class 13 A.O.C. O.E.G. Pullet
Class 14 Modern Game, Cock
Class 15 Modern Game, Hen
Class 16 Modern Game, Cockerel
Class 17 Modern Game, Pullet
Class 18 Indian or Jubilee Male or Female
Class 19 Ancona, Male
Class 20 Ancona, Female
Class 21 Buff Rock, Male
Class 22 Buff Rock, Female
Class 23 Rock, A.C. Male
Class 24 Rock, A.C. Female
Class 25 Pekin, A.C. Cock
Class 26 Pekin, Black Hen
Class 27 Pekin, White Hen
Class 28 Pekin, A.O.C. Hen
Class 29 Pekin, Cockerel
Class 30 Pekin, Pullet
Class 31 Leghorn, White, Male
Class 32 Leghorn, White, Female
Class 33 Leghorn, Black, Male or Female
Class 34 Leghorn, A.O.C., Male or Female
Class 35 Sussex, Male
Class 36 Sussex, Female
Class 37 Sebright, Gold, Male or Female
Class 38 Sebright, Silver, Male or Female
Class 39 Hamburgh, Spangled Male
Class 40 Hamburgh, Spangled Female
Class 41 Hamburgh, A.O.C., Male or Female
Class 42 Black Wyandotte, Male
Class 43 Black Wyandotte, Female
Class 44 White Wyandotte, Male
Class 45 White Wyandotte, Female
Class 46 Partridge Wyandotte, Male
Class 47 Partridge Wyandotte, Female
Class 48 Buff Wyandotte, Male or Female
Class 49 A.O.C. Wyandotte, Male
Class 50 A.O.C. Wyandotte, Female
Class 51 Australorp, Male
Class 52 Australorp, Female
Class 53 Rhode Island Red, Male
Class 54 Rhode Island Red, Female
Class 55 Minorca, Male or Female
Class 56 Rosecomb, Male or Female

Class 57 Orpington, Male
Class 58 Orpington, Female
Class 59 Marans, Male
Class 60 Marans, Female
Class 61 Any Other Variety, Male
Class 62 Any Other Variety, Female
Class 63 Any Variety Soft Feather, Cockerel
Class 64 Any Variety Soft Feather, Pullet
Class 65 Breeding Trio any variety hard feather bantams
Class 66 Breeding Trio any variety soft feather bantams
Class 67 Utility Bantam for laying purposes
Class 68 Selling class, Hard Feather Bantam, Male
Class 69 Selling class, Hard Feather Bantam, Female
Class 70 Selling class, Soft Feather Bantam, Male
Class 71 Selling class, Soft Feather Bantam, Female
Class 72 Gift Class, Large or Bantam, Male or Female (no entry fee)
Class 73 Children's Class. Any variety Bantam, Hard Feather, Male owned by a schoolchild
Class 74 Children's Class. Any variety Bantam, Hard Feather, Female owned by a schoolchild
Class 75 Children's Class. Any variety Bantam, Soft Feather, Male owned by a schoolchild
Class 76 Children's Class. Any variety Bantam, Soft Feather, Female owned by a schoolchild.

RULES AND POINTS TO NOTE

1. It is a Condition of Entry that the Society will not be responsible for the loss or damage of any exhibitor's property or exhibit.
2. Exhibitors are advised to check, before entering, any current Fowl Pest Regulations.
3. Classes with less than six entries will be amalgamated within the breed.
4. All stock must be cleared from the Auction Mart by 6.00 pm Saturday.
5. No duplications allowed.
6. Would exhibitors and visitors to the Show please note that no birds must be taken from the pens without the owner's permission. **This rule will be very strictly enforced.**
7. The Society will take 10 per cent of the sale price of any birds sold in the selling classes.
8. Judging will commence at 9.30 am.

The schedule is self-explanatory and any would-be exhibitor receiving one can tell at a glance the particular classes which will be staged for any particular breed. The rules and points noted are also self-explanatory. An example of an entry form has not been included here because different shows have their own particular type of form. Basically all you as an exhibitor need do is to list on the form the classes which you intend to enter, together with any relevant details including your name and address and send the form with the required entry fee to the show secretary. The show organisers will take care of everything from there on. You may receive your show-pen numbers beforehand or they may be handed to you on arrival at the show before the judging.

Washing and show preparation

Let us backtrack to the fancier in the penning room with the now tame and quiet cockerels and pullets which have been in their show pens for some two or three weeks. They are now ready for the final stage of show preparation: the stage of washing. There is an old saying that shows are won at home and this is true as far as the washing of your birds is concerned. Another old adage says 'washing will never make a bad bird into a good one, but can make a good one into a champion.'

Many homes have a utility room, be it a separate building or even part of the garage, with a sink with hot and cold water laid on. This is ideal for washing your birds ready for shows. However, if you do not have such a facility the birds will have to be washed in the kitchen sink or if all else fails then there is no alternative but large bucketfuls of warm water. Here we will assume that there is a suitable sink.

The first job before immersing the birds in the water is to wash their legs and feet with warm, soapy water, using a scrubbing brush to remove any dirt which has become hardened. It is no use putting a bird in the sink to wash it when the legs are full of muck because all the dirt will then be washed into the feathers. So, having first washed the legs and feet, the sink should be filled to the appropriate level with clean warm water. Carefully immerse the bird, making sure that the head and the top part of the neck remain very firmly above the surface! Then, taking the bird in one hand and the block of soap in the other, soap the bird all over, starting with the wings followed by the tail, back and body. By this time of course the bird will not only look terribly bedraggled but it will be full of soap. You therefore need to change the water. After refilling the sink with warm water, rinse off the soap as thoroughly as possible. Fill the sink with another change of water and give the bird a final rinse, immersing it gently up to its neck.

This describes the basic routine of washing, but only by experience will you find your own way of doing it. You may find that one particular brand of soap is better than another. Experienced show fanciers too have their own little secret bits and pieces that they add to the water at various stages of the washing process. For instance, many exhibitors showing white birds add a touch of 'blue' to the final rinse water – but it is important to gauge the right amount! Personally I use nothing but a good block of white soap when washing my birds, and they have won me many of the country's premier prizes.

Drying the birds

Having got the birds wet they now have to be dried. Again the method employed depends on your facilities. Some fanciers dry their birds with a hair-dryer, whilst others have a specially built box with wire netting over the front that they place in front of a fire or radiator, particularly the type that blows out warm air. Other fanciers put their birds in show hampers and leave them in front of an all-night burner, but this can be a risky business – if sparks should fly they would set the basket alight, or if the fire goes out and the birds remain wet, they could become chilled and die.

Some breeders have specially built drying compartments which work on the same principle as an incubator, hot air being blown into the compartment from below; the birds, on a strong wire-mesh floor, preen themselves as the warm air comes through.

Whatever drying method is used, care must be taken. Generally speaking you will find that your birds are somewhat docile at this particular stage. Once dry, they should be returned to their show pens where their feathers will web up again ready for the big day. There are many different views as to how many days before the show the birds should be washed, but it should be done at least three or four days beforehand.

It goes without saying that those of your birds intended for show must be in the peak of condition, fully feathered and in good health. If they are not, then the process of washing and drying will do them no good whatsoever and the job should never have been started in the first place.

So, with the bird(s) to be exhibited in super form, great condition and beautifully presented, show day is at hand. But how do the birds get there and how do they travel?

Travelling to the show

Anyone standing at the entrance to a poultry tent will see birds arrive in containers of all shapes, sizes and condition. It is alarming to see some exhibits, birds which have been specially

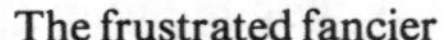

The frustrated fancier

prepared, with countless hours spent on them, being pulled out of a tatty old box. It is just as important to take your birds to shows in boxes which are roomy and clean, with clean bedding, as it is to give them the best facilities in the show cages at home. Use baskets or boxes, it does not matter which, providing there is sufficient room for the birds and above all they are clean. A basket is more robust than even a strong cardboard box but it represents a further financial investment. Whichever type of container you use – and especially if it is a wooden box – it must have a sufficient number of air holes.

The journey has begun; what happens on show day?

At the show

On show day the most important thing for the exhibitor to note from the schedule is the time of judging, in order to work out exactly what time to arrive at the show. Obviously this depends on the number of entries that you are going to exhibit, but most certainly your aim should be to arrive at the show at least an hour beforehand. If you do this you will have the advantage of unpacking your birds in quieter surroundings and giving them time to settle, whereas if you arrive at the last minute everything is hustle and bustle, exhibitors literally throwing their birds into the show pens over other people's shoulders, and the birds perhaps being judged within ten or fifteen minutes of being penned. This is not fair to the exhibits and is a complete waste of time.

In the knowledge therefore that you are arriving at the show in plenty of time, the first thing to be done is to find the pens that have been allocated to you. Check that they are secure, clean and free from dust. Very often these pens are used only once a year and are stored away in all sorts of odd places where they gather dust and dirt. Give them a quick wipe over, particularly if you have white birds. Having made sure there is litter in the pens, all is now ready for you to unpack your exhibits and carefully place them in the show pens.

However, before doing so a last quick touch-up is the order of the day. Anyone visiting a poultry tent before judging will see fanciers with all sizes of sponges and all sorts of bottles containing various assortments of liquids which are being sponged on to the birds' combs and faces. All kinds of lotions are used and whether

Section of one of Britain's largest poultry shows

one is better than another is difficult to decide. In fact if the bird is in peak condition it should not need any more than just a wet sponge over the head and comb to give that final touch. Just before putting the bird in the show pen, do a final check on the feathers, especially the sickle feathers; a quick rub down with a silk cloth will do wonders. If the bird has been correctly washed at the right time, the silk cloth will just bring out that extra little bit of bloom. I have never used any other method – a wet sponge for the head and comb and a silk cloth for the remainder.

The judge

All is now ready for the judge. At many of the country's leading agricultural and poultry shows the judges are people of long experience and members of the Poultry Club of Great Britain judges' panel. But though the judge is the boss for the day he is not unapproachable; most judges like to see a keen and enthusiastic new exhibitor who is willing to learn, because the beginner of today is the fancier of tomorrow. If a novice is willing to listen to the judge he can glean excellent advice. The show is one of the best places to learn, and the judge will be willing to tell the novice where he has been beaten and why. For instance, the judge very often will take the first-prize bird in the class and compare it with the second-prize bird to show a beginner how he made his decision. The judge will also be happy to give advice on breeding, indicating some of the important points to look for in your particular breed of bantam.

Show judges are usually very busy people and are sometimes expected to judge up to 300 different bantams in a morning. With such a number to sort out, obviously they must have a vast knowledge of bantams and be able to make up their minds very quickly. The first thing that they have to do at all shows is to award a first, second and third prize in the various classes and then choose the best of the various breeds exhibited for the particular breed-club special.

After the breed-club specials have been awarded the judges will then choose birds to receive awards such as the Best Hard Feather Bantam (applying to Game Bantams) and the Best Soft Feather Bantam, and at this stage of the show they are often awarding silverware as well as rosettes and prize cards. Judging completed, all that remains is for the cups to be presented and for the various exhibitors to assess whether the judge has made a good job or otherwise and to enjoy a few hours' gossip amongst themselves on various aspects of breeding, showing and even on how many chickens have been bred!

Back at home

The first thing to do on arriving back home is to give your birds a quick spray of an appropriate insecticide around the vent for mites, lice, etc. Most fanciers take great pride in their birds, keeping them totally free of pests, but there is always a risk at shows of your birds picking up parasites from the exhibits of a few fanciers who are far from particular about this aspect of bantam care; these little pests pass from bird to bird very quickly. A quick spray or dust will deal with this problem.

Your birds can now be returned to the run, or back to the show cage in the penning room if there are more shows in the near future. Then store away the travelling boxes or hampers, rather than leave them on one side where birds will perch on them or mice chew the corners. Neglected boxes and baskets look awful when brought into a public poultry tent. They are no advertisement for the fancy.

Cockerel boxes and night arks

Between shows, some of the professional exhibitors keep their birds in what are termed cockerel boxes. A cockerel box is a long, narrow movable run with separate compartments and runs on to the grass where the male birds can run out during the day and enjoy pecking and scratching, and return to the compartment to perch in the evening. These cockerel boxes are usually made by the fancier himself to his personal requirements. They are extremely useful little houses and besides being used for males can of course always be used for female bantams.

Other fanciers use night arks which have been specially converted, being divided into two separate compartments with runs attached. Between shows, birds are often put into these converted arks, where they keep themselves in the peak of condition.

Prize cards and rosettes

Nothing is more impressive than a wall full of prize cards, and with so much trouble and work involved in winning them they are worth preserving. Rosettes too are equally precious to the fancier and again care must be taken of them. A good idea is to scribble a little note on to the back of each prize card and rosette indicating which particular bird won it and any other details that you may wish to note. You will be surprised how often you refer to them and how helpful and useful is the information they bear.

If placing your prize cards on a wall, do put them somewhere out of the sunlight, or they will fade. Cover them with a sheet of clear polythene. Prize cards are normally placed in a prominent position where visitors, especially prospective buyers, can see them.

Showing eggs

Most poultry shows include an egg section and perhaps it is appropriate at this stage to give this important section of any poultry show a mention, if only to emphasise that anyone who keeps bantams (especially if they are not show birds) can become involved in the local society's egg show by exhibiting bantam eggs.

There are no hard and fast rules that certain breeds and types of bantams lay the best show eggs, but there are certainly breeds which are better for certain egg features than others. For instance, if it is your intention to show brown eggs then you are advised to keep Maran Bantams or Welsummer Bantams. Conversely Minorca Bantams lay good white eggs. There are of course other breeds that lay equally good white eggs, while tinted eggs can come from numerous breeds and from cross-bred bantams as well; very often it is the tinted eggs from a cross-bred bantam that win at the shows.

Here are details from the schedule of the egg classes at Ribble Valley Poultry Show. They are typical of the classes found at many of the egg shows today.

Egg Section
Plate of Three Hen Eggs, Brown
Plate of Three Hen Eggs, White
Plate of Three Hen Eggs, Tinted
Plate of Three Hen Eggs, three different colours
Plate of Three Hen Eggs, Speckled
Ideal Hen Egg
Ideal Bantam Egg
Contents, one egg to be broken (Hen)
Contents, one egg to be broken (Bantam)
Plate of Three Bantam Eggs, White
Plate of Three Bantam Eggs, A.O.C.
Plate of Three Duck Eggs

But how are eggs judged and what does the judge look for? The features assessed when judging are: Size, Shape, Shell, Bloom and Appearance, and in the Brown Eggs classes an added important heading – Colour.

Size in bantam eggs is important. They must not exceed $1\frac{1}{2}$ ounces each in weight – eggs over this size will be disqualified. Eggs that are too small, often described as 'birds' eggs', will never win prizes. The eggs should be of a good shape; they must not be round like table-tennis balls, nor must they be long and narrow. Dumpy eggs too are of no interest to a judge, nor those with a

Egg shape for showing: the centre egg is the correct shape. The egg at top left is too round; top right does not have a broad and a narrow end; bottom left is too long; and bottom right has two distinct ridges across the egg

ridge all the way round. The ideal shape is broad at the top, gradually coming down to a narrower, nicely curved point at the bottom. A good show egg should not be sharply pointed at the narrow end. The shells should be of good texture and not porous, and all the eggs on the plate should be of the same size, matching in colour and with a nice bloom and appearance; they should look fresh and natural. Some fanciers make the dreadful mistake of polishing their eggs; judges will exclude them from the prize list for this. The point that all the eggs must be similar is important, and a judge will place great emphasis on this. Obviously, it pays to try and collect all your show eggs from the same bantam.

Normally, a judge will not break any eggs when judging them, leaving this task until the 'contents' class is judged. The word 'contents' means contents only, and no attention is paid to the shape, size or shell of the egg. When showing in the contents class always make sure that the saucer your egg is placed on is free from dust, because that will show through in the white of the egg and can lead to disqualification. It tends to look as though it is a speck in the white.

What makes a good 'contents' egg? Firstly, the colour of the yolk is important. It is essential that it is rich in colour, that it stands out well from the white (the albumen) and moreover that it

Section of a typical egg show

stands well up from it. The three layers of white around the yolk must be clearly visible and two little pieces of what appears to be gristle, which keep the yolk suspended in the egg, should be visible; these are known as chalazae. The judge will not want to see blood spots, watery whites and pale yolks. You probably know already that birds which are kept in confined spaces generally produce eggs with pale yolks, but those running out on free range and picking up all the natural foods are the ones that produce eggs with rich deep-coloured yolks. These are the ones to use for the contents class.

Eggs intended for showing can only be kept for a certain length of time because of the effect on the air space in the broad end of the egg. As time goes along this becomes larger and larger and if a judge candles the egg this can immediately be seen. In any case, with age eggs tend to become very dull in the shell; so the fresher the eggs the more chance they have of winning.

Egg showing is an interesting hobby and many bantam exhibitors taking birds to the show also take along a couple of plates of bantam eggs for added interest.

6
Judging

Mr Judge has been briefly referred to already, in relation to his duties on show day and the circumstances in which he may find himself. A judge at a poultry show, or any other show for that matter, can be compared with a football referee. He is there to adjudicate, and is in control of the exhibits. He is invited by the show committee to sort out all the various exhibits and breeds – and his decision is final. He is boss for the day. As he (or she) examines each exhibit he assesses it and makes his own judgement, be it good, bad or indifferent, before placing the awards. Having placed the awards the judge should be able to explain to all the exhibitors, if necessary, the reasons for the decisions. Placing the awards, having a good lunch and running away is simply not done; all reputable judges stand their ground and if asked will substantiate their choices for the awards.

It has already been mentioned that poultry-show judges are not unapproachable – in fact they are often very experienced, and are helpful not only from an exhibiting point of view but also in giving valuable advice on the breeding of your stock, such as on how to improve various aspects of the breed, or how to select a breeding pen to eliminate certain faults.

But whether an exhibitor agrees or disagrees with the judge's decision the approach must always be the same. It is no use showing any frustration whatsoever at a judge's decision after it has been made. You should never forget that as an exhibitor you have read the schedule and signed the entry form agreeing 'to abide by the judge's decision'.

Who is a judge?

It is rather a bold statement but any fancier can become a judge. Of course some graduate to being judges sooner than others but there is no set time – it depends entirely on knowledge and experience and the rate at which this is acquired. Very often the particular standard of a fancier's own exhibits and the way in which they are presented at shows, together with his knowledge and experience of the breed, is acknowledged. Frequently it is acknowledged locally, and this means an invitation to judge a few classes at a local or a small members' show. The classes he will be asked to assess, on this his first occasion as a judge, will be based upon the breeds that he himself has bred and exhibited. There is no doubt that he will find the showroom to be a very lonely place when he makes his judging debut.

White Wyandotte bantam hen

On completion of his first exercise as a judge, the fancier's reaction is likely to be either that it was an enjoyable experience or a thoroughly unpleasant one. If it was enjoyable then there is no doubt he/she will want to judge at other shows and at some time in the future will probably apply for a judging test for inclusion on the Poultry Club of Great Britain Judges Panel. This panel is divided into specific categories and sections and the successful applicant will be placed in one relevant to his experience.

Judges really cannot be made – while a certain amount of theory is advisable, a judge cannot rely on theory alone; practical experience is absolutely vital. Lack of such experience often results in the overheard remark: 'Never won anything in his life.' With good practical experience and knowledge gained over many years, a fancier has a head start towards becoming a judge.

What does a judge do?

Every judge has his own particular way of judging exhibits, but there are a number of points applicable to all.

First, the judge should accept only invitations to judge breeds that he knows he is capable of assessing. He or she must never accept an invitation to judge breeds without sufficient experience or knowledge.

Secondly, the judge must read the schedule of the particular show very carefully to ensure that he/she knows exactly what is required and expected, especially with regard to the awarding of breed special prizes.

Thirdly, the judge must arrive at the show in good time and be prepared to put in a full morning of hard work.

Fourthly, when judging has commenced the judge must remember that each and every exhibitor has paid an entry fee, therefore every bird has to be properly and fairly assessed.

Fifthly, when judging has been completed the judge must be prepared to allow time for discussion with the exhibitors about the reasons for placing the various awards.

Judging a class

Let's assume you are about to judge for the first time and the great day has arrived.

Before commencing the actual judging, it is a good idea to take a walk along the front of the pens, quietly looking at each bird in its cage to see if there are any outstanding physical faults. For example, birds may be seen with a twisted toe, with a squirrel tail or a wry tail. At the same time you will note those birds which make a very favourable impression. Having completed this little exercise, you will know exactly how many exhibits are in the particular class and what the general standard is like.

You now go back to the start and prepare to commence the judging. Obviously, in some breeds the shape is all-important but in all breeds so is the type. Immediately before taking each bird from its cage you should assess the type. Then take each exhibit, in turn, from its pen and examine it. If you systematically check the toes, feet and leg colour, checking for a straight breast and no roach back, then check the comb, eyes, beak and wattles, in that particular order, there is little that you are likely to miss. In some

Examples of good and bad show feathers: *a* a good, typical, silver-laced Wyandotte feather; *b* a feather from the same species but showing faults around the edges and incorrect undercolour; *c* silver-spangled Hamburgh feather with a correctly shaped spangle, in comparison with an incorrect pear-shaped spangle in *d*

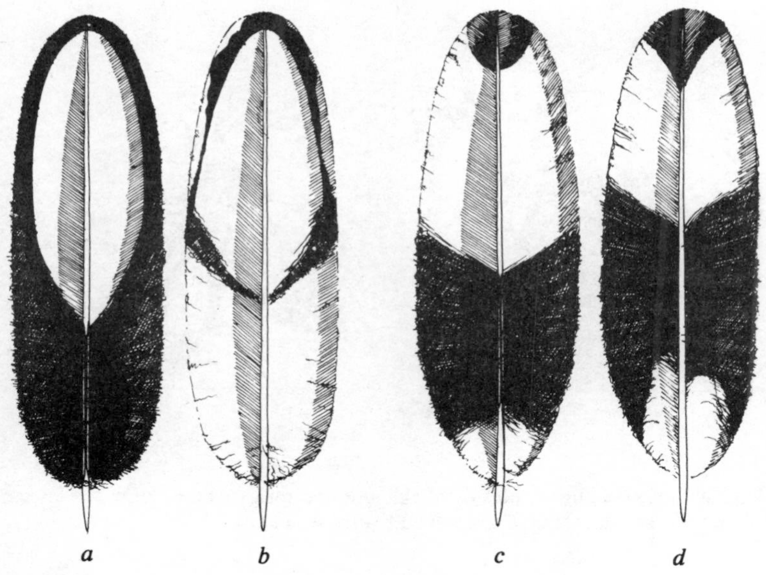

Typical faults leading to show disqualification: *a* sprig on comb; *b* knock knees; *c* bent toes; *d* squirrel tail; *e* roach back; *f* crossed beak

breeds lobes also play an important part. You now check each wing, not only to ensure that they are fully feathered but that the bird is not split-winged (which is a prevalent fault); you examine the markings, under colour and tail and also check that no unwanted insects are present. Finally, you must adhere to the laid-down breed standard and judge accordingly. On completion of the examination of each bird, you make either a mental note or a written one in your judging book, so that you can eventually, after examining each bird in the class, come to a fair decision on the awarding of the prizes.

The method of judging described above is a simple one and if used consistently will become automatic. It is important to remember to take *each* bird from its cage so that you never hear the complaint 'the judge never took mine out'. However poor a specimen a bird may be, you must still take it from the pen, even if the examination is somewhat brief!

Judging can be enjoyable, providing (as already stated) that you stick to those breeds and classes of which you have great experience and knowledge. Otherwise the exercise becomes difficult and it is then that problems arise.

Stewards

Perhaps it might be useful to outline here the various duties of the steward at a bantam show. So often people appointed as stewards are not given clear instructions and are at a loss as to what they should be doing.

Basically, the steward is a person appointed to help the judge, by handling the exhibits and doing the clerical work. The following rules should apply:

1 The steward must not be exhibiting under the judge to whom he is appointed as steward.
2 It is beneficial if the appointed steward is an experienced fancier. He can be of great help in taking bantams from the pens for the judge to inspect and, particularly, in bringing birds from other classes for comparison purposes. If he is able to handle birds competently and knows the various breeds it is a distinct advantage.
3 Another duty of the steward is to record the particular prizes given to the various exhibits in the judge's book and to ensure

that the secretary of the show is furnished with the official judging slips, duly signed, after the judging of the classes has been completed.

4 It is the duty of the steward to ensure that the exhibitors and the general public keep away from the judge whilst judging is taking place.

5 Finally, with the image of the show in mind, it is just as important for the steward as it is for the judge to be smartly dressed in a clean white coat.

7
Breeds and Breed Clubs

Some potential breeders and exhibitors are attracted to a particular breed. They may find the markings specially attractive or the feathered feet of particular breeds, or the crests and curves. For other potential breeders who have not made up their minds, this chapter may help them to decide.

Once you have selected a particular breed, then everything else should meet its requirements. If on the other hand you have first purchased the cabins and made the runs, you may need to buy a breed to fit the particular accommodation. So four areas should be considered – light, heavy, ornamental and rare breeds.

Light breeds

It is generally considered that some, though not all of the best egg layers are included in the classification 'light breeds'. This is certainly true of such breeds as Anconas, Hamburghs, Leghorns and Minorcas. These bantams are well known for their egg-laying potential, which has been proved over many years. Against this attribute, and to their detriment, light breeds do tend to be flighty, and consequently runs with higher fences (or better still, covered pens) are a necessity to prevent them getting out. Light breeds, generally, do not carry as much flesh as heavier breeds.

There is a wide variety of light breeds to choose from and in order to help you decide, the table on page 83 not only sets out each breed of bantam but gives the particular category in which the Poultry Club of Great Britain classifies it.

Heavy breeds

As already mentioned, heavy breeds, with their generally greater weight, do not tend to be as flighty as light breeds. It is also generally accepted that they do not lay as many eggs, and are much more prone to going broody. In fact, many of the heavy breeds crossed with a Silkie produce excellent broody bantams. It follows of course that many of the heavy-breed bantams make good mothers.

Very few bantams are bred for table use. However, should you wish to keep bantams for this purpose, you must use heavy breeds, such as the Faverolle.

Ornamentals

Many of the bantams most often admired at shows are those in the ornamental category. These birds have some special visual appeal such as elaborate plumage, which makes them quite different from the general run of bantams. Included in the ornamental category are such breeds as the Frizzle, with its curved feathers, the Pekin with its feathered feet, and the highly attractive Sebright with its eloquent markings and very jaunty appearance. Ornamental bantams are often referred to as 'Breeders' Birds'. Several of the breeds have done extremely well in the hands of top showmen and are often to be found amongst the top awards.

Rare breeds

There has over recent years been a tremendous revival in the rare breeds, with the result that many of the old-established breeds that were in very few hands can now be quite readily found. All the rare breeds come into one of the particular categories, being either a light breed, a heavy breed or an ornamental. Very great credit must be given to the Rare Poultry Society for their recent revival – it is most encouraging that so many of the breeds thought to be lost can now be seen again.

And for egg colour...

Certain breeds are particularly chosen by fanciers wanting to produce eggs of good colour for exhibition purposes. This section is somewhat easily defined; should deep brown eggs be required, then Marans or Welsummers are the two most popular breeds; Minorcas, Leghorns and Hamburghs often produce prizewinning white eggs. Light Sussex and Rhode Island Red bantams lay good tinted eggs.

The table below lists each breed and its particular category, together with the egg colour which can be expected.

BREED	HEAVY BREED	LIGHT BREED	ORNAMENTAL	EGG COLOUR
Ancona		●		White/cream
Australorp	●			Tinted to brown
Barbu d'Anvers			●	Cream/tinted
Barbu d'Uccle			●	Cream/tinted
Barnevelder	●			Brown
Brahma			●	Tinted
Faverolle	●			Tinted
Frizzle			●	Cream/tinted
Hamburgh		●		White
Indian & Jubilee Game	●			Tinted
Japanese			●	Cream/tinted
Leghorn		●		White
Marans	●			Dark brown
Minorca		●		White
Modern Game	●			Tinted
Old English Game		●		Tinted
Orpington	●			Tinted/brown
Pekin			●	Cream/tinted
Plymouth Rock	●			Tinted
Poland (Polish)			●	White
Rhode Island Red	●			Light brown/ brown
Rosecomb			●	White/cream
Scots Grey		●		White
Sebright			●	Cream
Sussex	●			Tinted
Welsummer		●		Dark brown
Wyandotte	●			Tinted

Breed notes

Here are further details on various breeds, to help with choosing one to keep. There is no intention of itemising every breed and its various show points, but some of the basic advantages and qualities of each are indicated.

Ancona

Beginners could do much worse than to start with Ancona bantams, despite their tendency to be rather flighty. They are appealing to the eye and well known for their egg-laying potential. Believed to have been imported from Ancona in Italy in the nineteenth century, these bantams can be found with either single or rose combs. Their markings, known as tippings, the white V-shaped tips at the end of each feather, are all-important at shows and a real challenge for the breeder. There are classes for these bantams at most poultry shows, and there is a well-organised breed club.

Australorp

A self-coloured bird and a useful breed for the beginner. It was

Ancona bantams

formed in the early 1920s by the late William Cook, and whilst it is a relatively new breed it has had its share of success in the show pens. Australorps are an easy breed to manage.

It must be emphasised that the colour of the plumage of these birds is beetle-green and not black. The only points that are black are the beak, legs and feet and it must be particularly noticed that the feet must have white soles. Even the eyes are black!

Type is one of the main essentials of this breed and potential breeders must be on the lookout for birds that are 'gypsy-faced' (with too much black where it should be red), because this is a serious defect.

Barnevelder

The Barnevelder bantam for some unknown reason is not one of the more popular bantams of today. Regrettably the deep brown egg colour of the standard-bred Barnevelders is rarely seen in its bantam counterpart.

Barnevelders are a breed that are good to manage but they have not had the same success as many other soft-feathered breeds at winning top honours in the showpen.

Belgian (Barbu D'Uccle and Barbu D'Anvers)

A beginner is somewhat confused by the terms Barbu D'Uccle and Barbu D'Anvers. The simple distinction is that the D'Uccle is always single-combed and has feathered legs. Belgian bantams exist in several colours and regrettably space does not allow to give descriptions of each and every sort. Such varieties as millefleurs, porcelain, quailes, mottled, and lavender are the most popular in the United Kingdom. Belgians are true ornamental bantams and have great attraction. They are one of the few breeds to have a beard, and this in addition to some having feathered legs, and the various varieties make them quite different from other breeds.

They have always been supported by a very active and well organised breed club, where advice is readily given. They do not need acres of ground – they can be kept in limited space with success, providing the management is correct.

Brahma

There are two varieties of Brahmas, light and dark. They have had some resurgence of popularity in the showpen, but have rarely achieved the very top honours. They are upstanding and somewhat sedate bantams, with triple or pea comb and have feathered legs and feet. One of the oldtime breeds, they are often depicted in old paintings.

Faverolle

This breed originates from the village of Faverolle in France and certainly comes under the category of 'heavy'. It has three varieties, ermine, salmon and white, and has certain unique characteristics. For instance the birds have such a luxuriant muff around the face that their earlobes and wattles are out of sight! It is also one of the few breeds that have five toes on each foot.

Frizzle

The Frizzle is a true bantam, with the most popular colours being black or white. It is easily recognisable, being quite distinctive with its curled feathers. Besides having an abundance of curl it is particularly important that good show specimens have got width of feather in addition. Perhaps not one of the most popular bantams Frizzles nevertheless are a great attraction when exhibited and certainly come under the ornamental classification!

Hamburgh

A breed which has made great strides over the last twenty years. Hamburgh bantams are now among the most popular at many of our shows and readily fill their classes. The Hamburghs are found in several varieties, silver-spangled, gold-spangled, gold-pencilled and silver-pencilled. They used to be called everlasting layers.

A good and attractive breed to manage, Hamburghs have had their share of top prizes. Markings play a very important part. The gold-pencilled females are particularly attractive and often are much admired when roaming on green grass. A most useful breed and another that is backed by an active breed club.

Indian & Jubilee Game

A heavy breed and a breed that has had its fair share of success at the top poultry shows. Again it is one of the few breeds that has a pea comb, but is a bird in which great substance is needed.

The Jubilee Game is white, the Indian Game dark, but that is the only difference. Shape and substance must be the same.

Gold-pencilled Hamburgh bantams (pullet breeders)

Japanese

Another true bantam, with different varieties. Japanese can be kept successfully on a limited space and also in fairly limited accommodation, provided that your management is good. But a word of warning: fertility is never as good in this breed as in many others. The reason is possibly the shortness of the male bird's legs!

Japanese are not among the most popular breeds around today. So far as show standards are concerned, the most important features are the head points, the birds' shape and tail carriage and the shortness of their legs, in addition to their type.

Leghorn

In complete contrast to the Japanese bantam, the Leghorn needs space. Of Mediterranean origin, again it has several different varieties. It is an old breed and has had fair success in the show pen, as well as being known for its egg-producing capabilities.

Although flighty, Leghorns are good to manage and their fertility is generally sound. Classes are provided for them at every show, and they can be recommended to would-be bantam breeders.

Maran

This is a miniature of the standard-bred bird. The Maran bantam is well known for producing dark brown eggs and is extremely popular with fanciers who aim to win in egg classes. It is quite easily managed.

Minorca

What has been said about Leghorns can in the main apply also to Minorcas, though there are certain adjustments in the show standards. Generally speaking, the accommodation and management requirements, and the potential, are similar. But a major difference from Leghorns is the lobe – and the care of lobes is essential with Minorca bantams if success is to be achieved at shows. Though known as 'black', the plumage should have a good green sheen.

Modern Game

Modern Game are among the smallest bantams, although classed as a 'heavy' breed. They have a fine body, are certainly one of the favourites and are indeed a showman's breed. If the intention is to show, and to win a cabinet full of silver, this is a breed to consider carefully. A good Modern Game bantam with the right type, style and reach, can always find its way to top honours, whatever its variety and colour – there are several that exist in good numbers today. They can be kept on limited space. They are not to be recommended, however, if you are looking for good egg-producers.

Old English Game

There are many, many colours of this favourite old bantam, and wherever poultry shows are held there are classes for OEG. Shape is essential, and another essential is that only judges with long experience of this breed should be appointed at shows. They are easily kept and will live anywhere, with proper management. They probably need less show preparation than many other breeds – a useful bantam for anyone.

Orpington

Orpington bantams are the counterpart of the standard-bred fowls of that name, and there are several varieties. Plumage must be in abundance and must provide an eyeful in the show pen. The breed is good to manage and certainly meets the requirements of most bantam keepers, although care must be taken not to get the birds too large.

Pekin

'Look, mummy, look at those birds – those bantams with feathers on their feet!' You can safely bet that the children are looking at Pekin bantams. A most popular soft-feathered breed, the Pekin is available in several different colours, making it extremely attractive. It is a very friendly bantam and can be kept in limited space, but care should be taken not to let it out into muddy runs during winter, or the feathers on the feet will be spoiled. These feathers are usually referred to as footings.

Plymouth Rock

A very easily managed bantam, found in different varieties, the most popular being the Buff and the Barred Rocks. This breed has

Buff Rock bantams

had its fair share of success and almost every show has classes for it. It is a breed ideal for anyone to keep and meets the requirements of most breeders and would-be breeders. Anyone purchasing stock, though, should make sure that the birds are sound in the wing, because slipped wings are a serious defect. So is the presence of any black or white in the wings of the Buff variety, and any white in the tail.

Poland (Polish)

There are several different varieties of these, but mention of them always brings to mind the crest, for which they are best known. Polands are not one of our most popular breeds but they are attractive. Owners should be extremely careful to preserve the crests at show time. The soundest piece of advice is to provide large feeding and drinking vessels, so that the birds do not rub and damage them.

Rhode Island Red

A grand old breed of bantam, and one where colour is the highest priority. It is a breed that is very easy to manage and it lays a good supply of eggs. There are classes for it at virtually every show, and it will do well anywhere.

Rosecomb

A true showman's breed, not necessarily one for the beginner. The comb, lobes, colour and type must be right. It needs extreme care, particularly from winds and strong sun, or the lobes will begin to blister and a good bird can be spoiled. Rosecombs win their share of top awards, but good management skill is needed.

Scots Grey

Not one of the more popular breeds, and more often found north of the Border than south of it. The colour and barred markings are the most important features of this breed. It could do with more supporters!

Sebright

Like the Rosecomb a gem of a show bird, but not necessarily a bird for the beginner. Sebrights are genuine bantams and are among the most attractive ones, jaunty in appearance with short

One of the author's Gold Sebright females – a winner of countless championships

backs; they have been much admired since Sir John Sebright bred them over 150 years ago. But they do require good management skills – and also patience, because fertility is not one of their strong points. A feature of the breed is that the males are hen-feathered – curved sickles or saddle-feathers being a serious fault.

Sussex
A grand old English breed and a miniature of the large Sussex fowl. Sussex bantams meet virtually every requirement: they can be kept almost anywhere, produce plenty of eggs and have their fair share of success in the show pen. Classes are available for them at almost every show. There are several different varieties, Lights being the most popular. A good all-round breed.

Welsummer
A useful bantam and one much sought after by breeders who keep bantams specifically for showing eggs – this breed is known for its deep brown eggs. It has not had a lot of success at shows, but is quite easy to manage and could do with more supporters. It is much admired when seen and is a breed that offers opportunities.

Wyandotte
There are several varieties of Wyandottes, and the white especially are often at the front of the queue when the top honours are handed out. A good white Wyandotte can be hard to beat. It is a graceful bird, its curves being an essential characteristic, and it is extremely popular. Though easy to manage, detailed and careful show preparation is required, especially washing.

Breed clubs

Having seen the advantages and disadvantages of some of the various breeds of bantams and noted in which section they fit, you will no doubt be keen to learn the finer points attributed to your particular breed of bantam. It is a sheer impossibility to give details of all the finer points of each breed but nevertheless some advice can be offered on where to go for this information.

Many of the breeds listed in the table on page 83 are supported by an active breed club. Each club is organised in a democratic way, and the officials normally consist of a president, chairman, secretary and treasurer with a responsible committee. Most of these officials have had many years of experience with that particular breed and are deeply involved in its promotion. The secretary is usually an active showman who can be found at many of the shows throughout the British Isles where advice will be freely given. The breed club has its standards, always available on application, and these list the various points which a judge will look for when judging that particular breed. Besides these there are two other lists – one giving defects of the breed, the other listing features which merit disqualification.

The breed club, which relies entirely on members' subscriptions and donations, holds an annual breed-club show, and in some instances regional shows, at which special rosettes and trophies are awarded. Furthermore, the breed club normally supports shows throughout the British Isles with special prizes in the form of rosettes and certificates and the secretary is always on hand to give advice – either written or verbal.

Needless to say, different breeds have different standards and it would need a separate book to list them all. However, it is sufficient to say that where breeds are dominated by colour, then more points are allocated for this feature, and those breeds which are dominated by their markings are awarded points which reflect their importance. There are various breeds where shape is the predominant factor, and consequently shape pulls more points with these birds. Details of the finer points and the complete breed standard, which is different for every breed, must be obtained from the particular breed-club secretary. Alternatively, you can apply to the secretary of the Poultry Club of Great Britain who, like the breed-club secretary, will be pleased to supply all the relevant information.

Faults in a bird

Whatever its breed, no judge will pass a bird which has particular physical faults. Again there are many and the list would be long if they were all included, but typical examples are the following: knock-knees, crooked toe, duck foot, wry tail, crooked breast, split wings, roach back and crossed beak. These are all physical defects; if any of these faults are present in any bird whatsoever, then it will be disqualified and quite rightly so.

In addition to having their own requirements on colour, markings and shape, different breed clubs place different emphasis on other points. For instance, some clubs place great emphasis on the correct shape of the comb, in others more importance is placed on type, carriage and style. It all depends on the particular breed, and again the best advice is to obtain the list of standards.

A second piece of advice (and perhaps the most useful) is, after studying the standards, to exhibit your birds at two or three shows and compare them with others in their particular class. Most judges will be only too willing to help and very often something that is visible is much more easily explained.

8
Health and Welfare

Observation is an important part of any bantam fancier's daily life. You need to look at your birds regularly in order to establish that the stud is free of any sickness or disease. One of the best times to check this point is at the morning feed when a sick bird can be quickly spotted. It will usually be huddled in a corner of the cabin looking thoroughly miserable, its wings down and the feathers ruffled. When food is put in the trough it will approach slowly without much interest and just pick at it.

Another good time for observing your birds is at night. Any bird which has not gone on the perch should be very thoroughly checked.

Diseases

This section covers the commoner ailments of bantams, those which as a breeder you must know about.

Avian tuberculosis Bantams that 'go light' usually have this disease. An affected bird will be nothing but skin and bone with a shrivelled comb. If you find one in this condition it should be killed and the carcass immediately buried or burnt.

Bacillary white diarrhoea This is commonly referred to as BWD and can cause high mortality rates, particularly with chicks. The germ is passed to the young bird through the yolk of the egg at hatching time. The disease causes the vent to be covered with a white diarrhoea. The only way to eradicate it is to check by blood tests which of the parent stock has the disease and then to eliminate the affected birds from the flock.

Black comb Sometimes a bird goes very dark in its comb. There can be several reasons for this, the most common of which is liver or heart trouble; in wintertime frostbite can have the same effect. An affected bird should be segregated from the rest of the flock and you should try to determine the cause of the ailment.

Bronchitis and colds These are usually caused by draughts in the poultry house and also by exposure to extreme weather conditions. Birds with bronchitis and colds can easily be identified by their running eyes and nostrils, together with sneezing and croaking (rattling) sounds in the throat.

Bumble foot This is caused through the birds alighting from perches and dropping boards which are perhaps too high from the floor, on to a hard surface. It is therefore important not to have the perch or dropping board too high from the cabin floor, and the latter should be covered with at least 3–4in of litter. Bumble foot is usually found in the heavier breeds of bantams.

This ailment equates with a corn in a human. It can, with care, be easily cut and squeezed out. The resultant wound should be well padded with a suitable dressing soaked in an appropriate antiseptic solution. The bird should then be isolated in a cage containing plenty of good dry litter until the wound is healed.

Canker If you notice a horrible, smelly and cheeselike substance coming from the beak of one of your birds, then it is very likely that the bantam has canker. After you have cleaned away the discharge, apply iodine.

Chills Bantam chicks are very susceptible to chills. Usually these develop because the chicks have got cold, possibly because they have not gone back under the brooder, or if outside have remained in the grass run instead of going into the covered area with the mother hen. The remedy is immediately to put the affected chicks in a box and put it in a warm place. Generally they recover rapidly if caught in time.

Coccidiosis A disease feared by all bantam breeders. It attacks young stock, especially between the ages of two weeks and four months. The coccidiosis parasite lives in the intestines of the birds. The first sure sign of its presence is when the chicks look weary and lethargic, with the wings down and the feathers ruffled. An examination of the droppings will reveal evidence of blood.

The sooner that coccidiosis is treated, the more chance there is of saving the chicks. One good remedy is to add sulphamezathine (obtainable from your veterinary surgeon) to the drinking water in accordance with the instructions.

Crop bound In nine cases out of ten the cause of birds becoming crop bound is overfeeding. There are some birds, just like human beings, that will simply eat everything put in front of them, and this is one reason why feeding has to be controlled. If you find a crop-bound bird, the quickest way of clearing the trouble is to dig up some worms from the garden and push two or three down the bird's throat. This is an old-fashioned method which has been proved successful time and again – the worms work their way into the crop and dislodge the blockage.

Egg bound Any bantam can suffer from egg bound – quite simply, it means that the bird is unable to part with the egg.

To assist an egg-bound bird, rub the vent with olive oil, place the bird in isolation and do not give it too much to eat. It may benefit from a gentle massage, but care is needed if you decide to give this treatment.

Fowl pest Fowl pest is basically pneumonia, and the symptoms are easily recognised. Affected birds will have droppings of a greenish colour, be very weary and have a continual nervous twitch of the head. They will not be interested in food, and if laying the egg production will have dropped dramatically. If this disease occurs in your flock you must *immediately* notify your local branch of the Ministry of Agriculture.

Paralysis There are many reasons why a bird can develop paralysis and as these are not always easily identifiable no immediate remedy can be given. In most cases a bird that develops paralysis has to be destroyed.

Prolapse This is caused by a bantam straining to lay an egg, with the result that certain of the intestines around the vent protrude. From my own experience I have found that the best way to deal with this is to bathe the area with warm water and gently push the protrusion back into place. If this situation arises repeatedly in the same bird it should be destroyed.

Vent gleet This is a particularly horrible and smelly discharge from the bird's vent. Once it is noticed, you should immediately clean up the area by washing with a suitable antiseptic solution, followed by an application of a little antiseptic cream.

Other problems

Moulting Any bantam fancier, particularly one deeply involved in showing, will be on the lookout for birds starting to moult. There is nothing more frustrating than a bird starting to lose its feathers two or three days before a big show.

Moulting is just nature's way of giving the bird a new coat of feathers and the process can occur from June onwards. Warm weather will tend to bring the moult forward, whereas a cold spell will delay it. Therefore moulting in bantams is a completely routine and natural matter, but while it goes on egg production will be negligible. It is recommended that the females should be placed on their own during a moult because, once again, a vigorous male can spoil the new feathers before they have even grown properly.

Egg eating The main cause of egg eating is simply boredom, and this usually stems from bad management. You should therefore have your birds organised so that this situation does not arise. If they are kept shut up in a cabin day after day, with nothing to occupy them, then a newly laid egg could be pecked, with the result that the birds get a taste for the contents of the shell and you will have a severe problem on your hands.

If egg eating does break out, one way of trying to prevent it is to make the nest box darker. It may mean putting in a specially enclosed nest box – the birds enter to lay their eggs but lack of light prevents them seeing the eggs once they are laid. Egg eating and feather pecking really go hand in hand – caused by birds having nothing to do.

It is possible to identify the egg-eating culprits by the stain of the yellow yolk on their feathers, but the best cure is not to let it happen in the first place.

Lice (and mites) These are great enemies of bantams. You should regularly spray or dust your birds with the appropriate remedy in order to keep these parasites at bay. Usually a spray or dusting around the vents and under the wings will destroy them. The best time to do this is at night, particularly for red mites, because they tend to lodge in cracks or conceal themselves under the perches and then crawl on to the birds during the hours of darkness.

There are some mites which get under the scales on bantams' legs, and this results in an infection known as 'scaly leg'. A good remedy for this is to rub the legs of affected birds with sulphur ointment.

Vermin The subject of vermin is an important one. The bantam breeder must be attentive because there are several enemies in this category. Mice, although only small creatures, can cause expensive damage. You know that they will nibble away at food bags, but you may not have realised that they can have a worse habit where bantams are concerned – nibbling away at the feathers of a bird. Far too often bantams are seen at shows with their sickle feathers, in particular, nibbled by mice. This simply means that mice have been present in, above all places, the penning room. Their presence here is disastrous, and has meant the difference between first and second prize on many occasions.

Rats too can be an absolute menace. Advice has already been given in this book on preventing them from living and breeding under poultry cabins by ensuring that the cabin is well raised off the ground, but they can nevertheless get into poultry houses from time to time. In addition to making a nuisance of themselves wherever the food is stored, they have been known to kill bantams and especially bantam chicks.

If mice or rats are seen in or around the poultry cabin, the penning room or the run, they must be caught as quickly as possible.

Foxes of course are well known for their ventures on a moonlit night into the poultry run, and it is therefore most important to ensure that all your bantams are secure by dusk. Foxes just occasionally raid bantam runs in the daytime, but usually it is done at night. Now and again a fox could destroy an entire cabin full of bantams in one raid – usually leaving the carcasses scattered around, with the heads bitten off.

In areas where foxes are prevalent and where daytime raids sometimes occur, fanciers build what is termed a 'fox tunnel' beside the cabin's pop hole and then hang a chain over the hole. Basically the idea is that the chain hanging over the pop hole will put the fox off because it believes it is a trap. Then, should the fox venture further and look inside the cabin, he will see the tunnel (measuring approximately 5ft in length, 12in in width and 15in in height) and now be convinced it is a trap and turn away. It is pure psychology but the ruse has been known to work.

9
The Next Move

Inspired by success in the show pen and the satisfaction derived from breeding prize-winning bantams, you will be full of enthusiasm to do bigger and better things. A long journey has been undertaken – from your first thoughts of keeping bantams to the ultimate success. It is at this stage, however, that you may feel you are at a crossroads, uncertain which way to go.

It is all too easy to believe that because success has been achieved with one breed, it will automatically follow with others. But there are many things which should be taken into consideration and which are often ignored. The further hoped-for success may not come, and then enthusiasm wanes because the original breed with which you were successful tends to become neglected and standards diminish.

Improve your stock – or diversify?

Whatever happens you should not make a quick decision. Many fanciers firmly believe that one breed is sufficient for anyone to handle, and are thus perfectly content to go on building success upon success. One-breed fanciers exhibit at shows throughout the British Isles, where their birds are consistent winners. These breeders have the time, they have the space, and moreover they are extending their knowledge year by year and consequently their stock is continually improving. They are able to experiment, perhaps by bringing in a male bird from another strain to see what progeny it can produce, and they are able to undertake these experiments without detriment to their existing high standards. Certain breeders and exhibitors build up a name for themselves which is automatically linked with a particular breed; these one-breed showmen are indeed a force to be reckoned with. Their birds can be bred as near to perfection as is possible and consequently success follows success.

It is a case therefore of deciding to be entirely satisfied as an expert one-breed fancier or facing the problems of keeping other breeds as well. But 'Jack of all trades and master of none' is a term often applied to exhibitors who show several breeds without ever achieving the high spots, and perhaps before considering an additional breed you should improve the existing one.

Improving stock

You should be aware of the standard and type of birds being exhibited against yours, and as already mentioned could be doing some experimenting on the side with the possibility of a new blood line. It is of course out of the question to buy birds here, there and everywhere, but sometimes an experiment with an outcross can pay handsome dividends. There are times when new blood has to be introduced into the flock, and rather than simply buy a bird and chance it, it is far better to have experimented quietly for one year to establish exactly what sort of progeny are produced. By doing this any risk is very much reduced. Again, you might have noted that in your existing stock there is some particular weakness: you could bring in a bird which is strong in that particular point, in order to improve matters. A little experimenting on the side will prove whether your idea was a good one, before introducing the bird into the flock.

You should always be aware of current trends. Whilst the breed standards are laid down, nevertheless trends do develop, and the fancier must be in a position to move with these if the major prizes are to be won.

Everything considered therefore, it is much harder to keep at the top of the tree than to climb up it. When a fancier is on the top branch everyone is there ready to have a go and competition becomes intense. In order to keep that position at the top it is necessary to maintain a breeding policy like the one described above.

There is therefore the on-going problem of improving your existing stock. With this in mind, is it a correct and sensible decision to take on one or two additional breeds?

An additional breed?

If another breed is taken on, it can be immediately said that everything is doubled and if two extra breeds are involved everything is trebled. Sit down and think seriously about it. Presuming that you have given due consideration to taking on an

THE
NATIONAL
FIRST
ALEXANDRA

additional breed, you must realise that double the accommodation space is required, particularly in the runs and cabins; this also means doubling the equipment, in the form of nest boxes, feeding troughs and water fountains. Furthermore, another breed means sometimes doubling the weekly or fortnightly order for poultry food. The total cost of your hobby is automatically doubled if it is to be run on the same lines and with the same determination as your existing breed.

But cost does not end there. More show pens will be needed, meaning more space in the penning room, and additional baskets and boxes for the shows. The entry fees will be doubled too. And unless the whole project is carried out efficiently, it could mean less prize money coming in. Prize money is not the sole objective, but it does help!

It is perfectly true that many fanciers take on an extra breed and manage very well. But, apart from cost, it can create problems in the breeding season. Instead of having, say, four breeding pens solely devoted to one breed, you allocate two to each of them; consequently there is not only a reduction in the number of chicks produced by each breed but often a lowering of quality. Furthermore, the two breeds have at some time or other to be separated and this is where the problem starts. Space is therefore a most important factor, and its allocation must be very seriously considered before any decision is taken. The all-important question is 'Is there room to do it?'

By using all your space in this way, you are reducing your scope for experimentation with an additional outcross; furthermore, you will have less time for building a comprehensive and detailed knowledge of the original breed.

These then are the pitfalls involved with the taking on of an additional breed. It would be a pity if all your efforts to establish a prize-winning strain are spoilt by a false move. Make sure your decision is the right one, so that you are able to continue to enjoy the breeding and showing of bantams; may good fortune be with you whatever you breed – and wherever you travel and exhibit.

Author with another Hamburgh winner. This particular bird won Breed Championship at the Poultry Club Championship Show, Alexandra Palace, London two years running. It also bred the cockerel that won first prize in London in 1978 and at the Royal Show 1979

Glossary

AOC Any other colour.
AOV Any other variety.
Axial feather The small feather between the primaries and the secondaries.
Barring Equal-sized alternating stripes, as fine as possible, of two definite clear colours across a feather.
Beard Feathers under the throat of certain breeds of bantam.
Beetle green A definite green lustre seen on self-coloured black birds or birds with black markings.
Bloom Often used to describe the fresh look of eggs being exhibited.
Brassiness A yellow tinge sometimes found on white birds, particularly on the back and the saddle. Often caused through being exposed to the sun or sometimes by wrong show preparation.
Chicken feather The plumage before a bantam has grown its adult feathers.
Cockerel breeder A bird specially selected to produce good male birds.
Condition The bird's state of health, particularly its head points and its fitness.
Crest Feathers, globular in shape, on top of the head – as seen in Poland bantams.
Crooked breastbone Breastbone with bend or dent, often the result of the birds roosting on narrow perches at a very early age.
Crooked toes Usually caused by in-breeding.
Cushion Feathers which give height to the rear part of the back.
Dished lobe A lobe that is hollow in the centre.
Dubbing Removal of the comb, ear lobes and wattles by cutting (game bantams).
Duck-footed A bird which has the back toe out of line with the middle toe.
Frosting A marginal trace of colour round the edge of a feather.
Ground colour The basic colour of a feather.

Gypsy face A very dark purple head.
Hollow comb A depression or dip in a comb.
Knock-kneed A bird which does not stand correctly – the legs come together at the hocks.
Lacing The markings which follow the outline of a feather, eg on Sebrights.
Lopped comb A comb which falls over to one side.
Main Sickle feathers The two long feathers in the tail of a cock or cockerel.
Mossy Describes markings which are too blurred or faint, not definite enough.
Mottled Ends of feathers which are a different colour from the ground colour, but are not required to be of any particular size, shape or definition.
Muff A cluster of feathers on each side of the face – seen in Belgian and some game bantams.
Pad The central underpart of the foot.
Pencilling Found in two forms. Refers to the stripes going across a feather, as in Pencilled Hamburghs.
Peppering Spots of a darker colour over a light background, eg black markings inside a Sebright's tail.
Primaries The section of wing flight feathers hidden when the wing is closed.
Pullet breeder A male or female selected to produce good females.
Quill The stem of a feather.
Roach back A bantam which has a hump on its back.
Secondaries The section of wing flight feathers visible when the wing is closed.
Self-coloured Bantams of one colour.
Serrations The distance between the spikes of a single comb.
Sheen A glossy surface, particularly on birds with black plumage.
Side sprig A spike on the side of a single comb.
Smut Dark colour or dark patches which should not be there.
Spangling A definite spot of colour at the end of a feather.
Split wing Wing with a gap between the primary and secondary feathers that is not caused by moulting.
Squirrel tail A tail which comes over the back of the bantam instead of being at the correct angle.
Thumb mark Sometimes found on the side of a single comb.
Ticking Small marks different in colour from the ground colour.

Tipping A different colour at the end of a feather.
Type The carriage, deportment and shape of a bantam as laid down in the breed standards.
Undercolour The colour of that part of the feather nearest to the skin, which is not normally visible.
Wry tail A tail which is carried to one side.

Acknowledgements

There are indeed many people who have encouraged, guided, and helped me in my many years in the bantam show world. This book is dedicated to them all in acknowledgement of this and for the many happy hours spent with them.

My special thanks to my wife Roberta for her endurance, to Paul Russell for the line drawings, *Poultry World*, Jeremy Makinson and Wally Talbot for the photographs, and to Jill Hargreaves for so kindly typing yet another manuscript.

Index